Sheets, pillowslips, bolster cases, towels, the Christmas presents. Old faded blankets and even two discoloured and torn old pillows came under my scrutiny, but my little box had vanished, and with it the kitten box. Oh God, who could have taken it? Nothing could replace Mummy's scarf, the lock of her black silky hair or my Mabel Lucie Attwell annual. They were all I had of her and now they were gone. I made my way downstairs to my new 'bedroom'. The warm glow of the fire had become a flickering orange flame that reached out to scorch my very soul, as it did whenever I remembered what my father had told me, that I had caused Mummy's death.

CAROL-ANN COURTNEY

A SHILLING FOR THE AXE-MAN

A SIGNET BOOK

SIGNET

Published by the Penguin Group
Penguin Books Ltd, 27 Wrights Lane, London w8 5tz, England
Penguin Books USA Inc., 375 Hudson Street, New York, New York 10014, USA
Penguin Books Australia Ltd, Ringwood, Victoria, Australia
Penguin Books Canada Ltd, 10 Alcorn Avenue, Toronto, Ontario, Canada m4v 3b2
Penguin Books (NZ) Ltd, 182–190 Wairau Road, Auckland 10, New Zealand

Penguin Books Ltd, Registered Offices: Harmondsworth, Middlesex, England

First published 1993
3 5 7 9 10 8 6 4 2

The characters and events depicted in this book are real. The
names, however, have been used fictitiously. Any resemblance in
name to any persons, living or dead, is entirely coincidental.

Typset by Datix International Limited, Bungay, Suffolk
Set in 10/13 pt Monophoto Times
Printed in England by Clays Ltd, St Ives plc

Acknowledgements

The author would like to thank the publishers listed below for their permission to use lyric extracts from the following songs.

'Beyond the Blue Horizon' (Famous/Chappell) and 'Black Moonlight' (Famous/Chappell), by kind permission of Warner Chappell Music Limited; 'A Blossom Fell' (Barnes/Cornelius/John), by kind permission of Mistletoe Melodies, 1 Wyndham Yard, London WIH 1AR; 'Blue Moon' (Richard Rodgers/Lorenz Hart), by kind permission of EMI Music Publishing Limited; 'The Continental' (Herb Magidson/Con Conrad), by kind permission of Chappell Music Limited; 'The Echo of a Song' (Mendosa/Lawrence Wright), by kind permission of EMI Music Publishing Limited; 'Goodbye' (Graham/Stolz), 'Let's Face the Music and Dance' (Irving Berlin) and 'My Funny Valentine' (Richard Rodgers/Lorenz Hart), by kind permission of Chappell Music Limited; 'Oklahoma' (Richard Rodgers/Oscar Hammerstein II), by kind permission of Williamson Music; 'Someone to Watch Over Me' (George and Ira Gershwin), 'Spread a Little Happiness' (Vivian Ellis/Richard Myers/Greatex Newman), 'This Is My Beloved' (Robert Wright/George Forrest) and 'Trees' (Oscar Rasbach/Joyce Kilmer), by kind permission of Chappell Music Limited.

Preface

It is natural for people to need to love and be loved; we do not expect physical and mental violation in return for seeking affection. But, as the alcoholic hides the bottle, the paedophile makes his victim his secret partner to serve his addiction. The bottles lie discarded in their thousands, some fractured, some with their remains fermenting, some completely shattered. I have chosen to uncork the bottle that is myself, and what I have found is a very lethal potion indeed. It may be a brew that society will find very hard to swallow.

This book is dedicated to the many thousands of abused people in the world today. It has been written to help us try to take our first faltering steps out of the shadows where we have lived with guilt, self-deprecation and despair. We must now move forward to try to reinstate the natural order, to rebuild self-esteem and to find love and affection so long denied us.

My thanks go to all those who work tirelessly on Esther Rantzen's Helpline, especially to Janet Pardue and Kathryn Warren, all social workers, counsellors, police, doctors and nursing staff. Special thanks to my own GPs.

Thanks also to the entire Courtney family, and to Jan Carew, Susanna Collins, Stephanie Dickinson, Sue

Dixon-Eccles; the late Marianne Evans, Cassie Jenkins, David Jenkins, Kate Lloyd, Janet Marsh, Hilda Owens, Betsan Roberts, Jan Taylor, Barbara Watkins, Karen Williams, Elsie Wolahan and the Roman Catholic Church.

Finally, my thanks to all at Penguin, especially Tony Lacey and Andrew Barker, and special thanks to my editor, Barbara Horn.

Carol-Ann Courtney
September 1992

A child at night seeks comfort from
the warmth of a parent's body,
The terrors of the night are blotted out,
Only to return in a dream . . .

David Alun Courteney

Prologue

And still the orange candle glowed ... its amber glow shone through my dreams, its flame gentle now.

The pyracantha tree that climbed, tap-tap-tapping, past my window had become my friend, a friend who had introduced me to an aspect of the seasons of which I had hitherto been only vaguely aware.

The fruit and vegetables sold on the market stalls outside my home; the hot pavements and long summer playing hours; the shortness of the winter days; freezing weather, chapped legs, hands and lips: these had depicted the seasons in London. My world of concrete and clay, my home, mother, father, grandmother, brothers and sisters, my London. Another world, another time ...

There spring was heralded by daffodils and tulips on the market stalls and in the parks. Lemons would appear for Pancake Day and Forrester's, the local sweet shop, would proudly display Easter eggs, some in multi-coloured foil wrappings, others cellophane-wrapped in boxes, with red, pink and violet sugar flowers blooming on their rich, shiny brown chocolate shells. On Easter Sunday morning, after the painted hen's eggs had been impatiently consumed with 'soldiers', our hands would gently ease apart the halves of the chocolate shells and they'd appear in all their splendour like two exquisite tortoises to be stroked and admired – our warm fingers dulling their shiny surface until, at last, we'd succumb to temptation and place the first long-resisted piece on our equally warm, welcoming tongues!

Our Nature Table at school was another spring delight as the nasturtiums we had planted in earthenware flowerpots pushed their orange-red heads upwards as each bud opened, and the mustard seeds were transformed from tiny black beads into heads of deep green cress that looked like a miniature forest as they stood miraculously on their blotting-paper beds.

Summer . . . ah, summer! With the stalls smelling of lettuce, cucumbers, spring onions and tomatoes. Cherries in a brown paper bag, their red juice bleeding through; cherries, whose green stalks could be hung over your ears – deep ruby earrings – until the temptation to peck at the precious 'jewels' became too great to resist. Grapes were only for the film stars, who lay on red velvet *chaises-longues* trimmed with gold while their slaves held the clusters over their mouths and they bit nonchalantly at the fruit, like Cleopatra in the film we'd seen. We hadn't liked gooseberries even when Granny amazed us by telling us that it was only the hairs on a gooseberry that stopped it from being a grape. We tried again and unanimously agreed that Granny's taste must be going, along with her eyes, hearing and memory; quite where they were going to we never understood! Plums were fairly easy to get, but strawberries and raspberries were rarities to be savoured.

Those long, hot summer days found us making occasional trips to the Tower of London. Dares to lay our heads on the bed in which the two little princes had been suffocated by their wicked uncle, Richard III, were thwarted by an official, who'd scare us by suggesting he'd lay our heads on the block! Traitors' Gate and the Bloody Tower filled our imaginations with excitement – and fear, which no one would admit to.

The British Museum enthralled us, especially the Egyptian Rooms with their mummies and pharaohs, but it was 'Ginger' we loved most. Ginger lay in his glass case on his side, his water jugs on the sandy base, his skin like a jacket potato, and tufts of ginger hair still evident. Certain extremities were divorcing themselves from Ginger – a toe or a finger threatened to fall on to the sand at the bottom of the case. A rag covered his lower torso and whatever modesty the poor soul had a right to, if one has such rights when thousands of years old, but, to my deep embarrassment, my brothers would walk stooped and crab-like around the glass coffin to see if his 'willie' had come off yet!

If these macabre sojourns were the highlights of our holidays, we also enjoyed trips to the Lido swimming pool and Regent's Park Zoo, and, best of all, an annual trip to Battersea Fun Fair on August Bank Holiday Monday. Twice we went in a charabanc to Southend for the day. The first sight of the grey expanse of choppy sea and its pebbled beach and pier filled me with an excitement I'd never known before. The rest of the summer found us playing on bomb-sites, making 'house' out of what had once been people's homes, and creating our own amusements in the streets around us.

We, the children who lived between Holloway and Pentonville prisons, understood that the wages of sin was death. A short walk took us to Tollington Park, to a house where the murderer Frederick Seddons had lived and poisoned his lodger with arsenic. A big dare was to run up the eight or so steps to the front door and down again. I did this twice and was rewarded with blackjacks and fruit-salad sweets for bravery.

Another sinister walk, slightly longer, was to Hilldrop Crescent, a journey that took us past Holloway Prison, which the boys always said looked a bit like the Tower, not 'Her Majesty's Rest Home for Shady Ladies', as the bus conductors used to call it! Studying the house here that was so like Seddons' in Tollington Park, I was about to ascend the steps – the prize for this feat of courage was a packet of fruit gums – when a fat, elderly lady appeared at the top, stopping me dead in my tracks.

'Whaddya want?' she demanded, folding across her chest arms whose pallor and consistency reminded me of the tripe that used to make us feel sick as it lay on its slab in the butcher's. Her face and legs seemed to have the same pliant white texture.

'We're looking for our auntie,' one of the boys shouted up to her.

'Auntie . . . er . . . Christine,' I added.

'Do this auntie 'ave anuvver name?' The white jelly-like mass was descending the steps now in an odd sideways motion. Her large floral pinafore imprisoned the fleshy mass and a grubby turban encapsulated whatever hair she might have had. Her face, when she eventually reached street level, was surprisingly pretty for an old lady and a very fat one at that.

'I can't remember her other name,' I lied. 'But I do know she lived in the same house as this one, Dr Crippen's.' I pointed in the direction of the house from which she'd emerged.

'You don't say. Well, there's a fing!' She was smiling

at us now. A white arthritic thumb and two fingers pinched at her bottom lip, exposing the only colour she seemed to possess, a half moon of shiny pink gum. ''Ow long ago was yer auntie livin' in Crippen's 'ouse then, eh?'

'Oh, she was there last Christmas!' one of the boys said.

'She'd a bin a clever bugger an' no mistake!' The fat lady began to laugh a bubbly sort of laugh that sounded like our toilet after you'd pulled the chain and its noise was subsiding. 'Crippen's 'ouse was along there.' She pointed a large white pork-sausage finger, indicating further along where the road curved. 'They pulled down 'is 'ouse an' put them flats up, see! That were years ago an' all, so don't come the ol' acid wiv me, ya little buggers. You'll get sores on yer tongue if ya tell lies. Now then, you can go an' git me two pound o' spuds, 'alf a split tin an' five Woodies. Turn left round the crescent an' you'll be on the Brecknock Road. 'Ere's 'alf a dollar.' She withdrew a large brown moth-eaten purse from somewhere in the depths of her expansive pinny and gave me half a crown.

We were about to head off in the direction she had indicated when suddenly a white, squid-like hand pulled me back.

'I weren't born yesterday, ya know. Leave yer bruvvers 'ere an' 'op it!'

The boys looked scared and I raced around the corner to the shops. I must have been back in five minutes. The boys were leaning against her wall as I rounded the crescent, and I could see she was nursing a tabby cat similar to our cat, Prowler, in her arms.

'That were quick, gel. 'Ere, git yourselfs a lolly each.'

She took her purchases and put tuppence into each of our hands. 'Come an' see me again some time . . . Doctor bloody Crippen an' all if ya wants . . .'

We beat a hasty retreat as the lavatory's cistern began its gurgle up the stairs.

Autumn brought the harvest and the biggest marrow we could find would be taken proudly to school for the Harvest Festival. Pomegranates were special. For us, the coming of Guy Fawkes night and the thick London smogs were always associated with this fruit. We'd pierce each tiny segment of its pink flesh with a pin, the fruity richness filling our mouths and bringing with it hopes for the coming winter and Christmas.

Carrots, onions, swedes, parsnips and turnips – winter stew – almost overnight gave way to the delights of walnuts, brazils, hazelnuts and chestnuts, oranges and tangerines, boxes of dates and figs. Mistletoe and holly were hung above the fruit and veg stalls, and the paraffin lamps that lit up these seasonal delicacies seemed to take on a warmer glow than usual. The best smell of all came with the pine-needles as the Christmas trees arrived, to lean drunkenly against the sides of the costermongers' barrows.

Christmas crackers, paper chains and other decorations now appeared in Forrester's shop window. 'Snow Houses' and annuals, boxes of chocolates with beautiful pictures and satin bows were displayed along with boxes of cigarettes and cigars. White net Christmas stockings and chocolate Santas would cause the boys to stop outside saying 'I'm having that . . . and that . . . and that!'

The yellow sulphuric glow of the smog excited us,

even though it sometimes made our throats sore. Sometimes, if the smog was very bad, the buses and cars would be abandoned in the road and we would say that the earth had stood still! No matter; the smog, enveloping us in a world of our very own, could never deter us from going into the street outside the Mansions where we lived and along the road to the market stalls. We didn't venture any further, for in those streets Jack the Ripper could be abroad once again!

Everyone's granny had had some dealings with Jack at some time, often escaping from his grip by only a 'hair's breadth'. Jack the Ripper was ageless. Our journeys to see the Seddons' house in Tollington Park and Dr Crippen's in Hilldrop Crescent now became ominous pilgrimages, never to be undertaken when winter's cloak enfolded us.

One Christmas found us caught up in our mother's activities after the trial of two men for the murder of a policeman. The men were Christopher Craig and Derek Bentley. We listened as our mother explained that it was Christopher Craig who had actually shot the policeman, but Derek Bentley who was to be hanged for the murder. Derek Bentley, it seemed, had said 'Let him have it, Chris'. Derek said he'd meant surrender the gun, but Christopher Craig said that he thought his friend meant let him have the bullets. Christopher Craig was only sixteen and too young to hang, but Derek Bentley was nineteen and so he was sentenced to death.

Mummy and her friends had bought lots of red exercise books and we walked miles, knocking on doors, asking people to sign a petition to stop Derek Bentley going to the gallows for a murder he hadn't committed.

7

Nearly everyone we asked signed their names in those books. It didn't seem fair to us children that Derek Bentley should hang, and we believed that Mummy and her friends would somehow save him with the hundreds of names they'd collected in the red books and handed in to the Home Office. But Derek Bentley was hanged.

That same year my mother and her friends bought more of the red books after a man with a very posh name was found guilty of the murder of lots of women, whose bodies he had hidden in his house at 10 Rillington Place. (We'd discovered this wasn't on our territory, so made no attempt to seek it out. It was probably the same sort of house as the ones in Tollington Park and Hilldrop Crescent anyway.) The man's name was, of course, John Reginald Halliday Christie. Three years earlier his evidence had helped to convict a young man named Timothy Evans for the murder of his wife and child, a crime for which he had been hanged and to which Christie now confessed. But what could Mummy and her friends do, since poor Timothy Evans was dead? Were they also trying to stop this man with the long name going to the gallows?

Mummy told us that this new petition was to demand that Timothy Evans be given a royal pardon and his body taken from the prison and buried in holy ground. This seemed poor consolation to us, and when she said that 'Mr Christie should die slowly and painfully', we were shocked. We had always believed in her deep conviction that no one should hang. Now she explained to us perplexed and disappointed children that there were different types of murders and reasons for committing them. 'Mr Christmas Holiday', as one of the boys dubbed him, was hanged at Pentonville on a hot, sunny

8

morning just before school broke up for the summer holidays. Our mother went to the prison that morning to 'see justice done'. Grown-ups were certainly changeable people, even Mummy! Just quite how she would change in the next two years we would never have believed.

My baby sister, Anna, had been born shortly after my mother had undergone surgery for a brain tumour. Oh, how jealous I'd been when I heard that the baby was a girl! The boys and I had had to go into a children's home, which compounded my resentment at the birth of this new female rival.

My father changed too, and our whole world was turned upside down. He had been discharged from the Navy with cancer and had had a lung removed. The handsome stranger who'd spent most of his time at sea, returning occasionally, armed with rare and beautiful presents, and whose home leave always seemed so short, was no longer the father we'd known and loved so much. He began to drink a lot and argue with my mother. Once I heard her say that she 'could kill him'! This frightened me and I remembered her words about murder: there were different types and reasons for them, although no one should commit such a sin.

We heard about one of these different types of killing when a pretty young blonde named Ruth Ellis was convicted of murdering her lover, and was sentenced to be hanged in Holloway Prison. Once again my mother became involved in a petition, but it was her friends who took the lead in buying the red books. It was summer again, and Mummy and I went out to collect the signatures of people who were against the hanging;

everyone was talking about a reprieve. It was like old times as I walked through the streets with my mother. She tried to explain that Ruth Ellis shooting her boyfriend was a 'crime of passion' and if she had lived in France, she probably would only have gone to prison for a few years.

'If you killed Daddy, would that –?' I began.

'Oh, baby, what a thing to say! I love your daddy very much. If you've heard us say unkind things to each other, it's because of our operations. But we're both getting better now, and we'll soon be a happy family again!' She hugged me to her and knocked on a door, book and pencil ready. I could never understand how everyone in the world seemed to be signing Mummy and her friends' petition to stop Ruth Ellis hanging and yet no one in the world did stop it.

It was another July, another hot, sunny day, when the crowds and mounted policemen began to pass the Mansions. My father didn't want Mummy to go to the prison and neither did Granny. My mother had fed the baby, who was outside in the yard fast asleep in her pram.

'Are you going?' I whispered to my mother.

'Yes, but don't tell the Devil and his disciple!' she giggled. She had often referred to my father and grandmother in these terms lately. 'Be a good girl and hurry the boys up for me. You'll make sure they're safe across that road?'

I nodded. Granny was pouring Daddy a cup of tea as I started to shepherd the boys out of the door on their way to school.

'We'll be so early the caretaker won't be bloody up!' the boys complained. 'Here, Mum gave us sixpence each, go on!' They accepted the money gratefully and didn't even ask where I was going as I saw them across the road. The sun was shining and they'd got sixpence!

I caught sight of my mother as she walked along the Holloway Road and followed her up past the Nag's Head. I turned into Parkhurst Road and could no longer see her. The crowd was thick and angry and I became frightened. Ruth Ellis was due to hang at 9 a.m., but there was still time . . . I decided to return to school.

Days of hangings had a strange, mixed atmosphere for us, an atmosphere so tangible you felt that you could almost reach out and touch it. Excitement and sadness as we thought about the black cap, the noose, the trapdoor, the hour during which the prisoner would have to hang on that rope. Outside of the prison one sheet of white paper – the white lifeless corpse – surrounded by the blood of a thousand red exercise books. One white cold hand writing to tell the world that justice had been done, the execution had taken place. Thousands of warm hands that had grasped at pencils, asking that no blood be spilled . . . the sombre toll of the church bells and the special assembly at school; prayers offered up to God to show mercy to the sinner now departed and for whom the bells tolled.

On these days I would think about the prisoner and what his or her thoughts would be. At five minutes to nine Ruth Ellis was alive and she knew that at five past nine she would be dead. It always frightened me, this appointment with death. However sorry I felt for the people who had been murdered, it was some consolation that they didn't know the time, place and date that they would die.

I was not to know that Death had placed an entry in her diary for me: almost exactly a year later she took my mother.

1

The evergreen tree and the orange candle, warm on my face, awoke me. No – it was the pyracantha tapping on the window, the sun's warmth and the birds calling their reveille through the amber glow of the orange, pink and yellow chintz curtains.

Four months had passed since I had been settled in this home far from London. Oh, those first weeks! A whirlwind of being taken to see an Auntie Ada and her daughter, Rose (whom I hadn't liked very much), in Bow, in the East End of London, then on to Guildford in Surrey, where my new Uncle Desmond and Auntie May lived. Neighbours and friends of my new foster-parents, Arthur and Kathleen Oakes, had made me feel very special and welcome, taking away some of the pain I still suffered at being separated from my brothers and baby sister, Anna, whom I had come to adore. Mrs Oakes had said that I should call her 'Mums' and Mr Oakes 'Dads', but the most I could ever manage was 'Mm' and 'Der'! The only cloud on the horizon was the Oakeses' son, Gordon, whose endeavours to ignore me and show his disapproval of my having taken up residence in his parents' home had been extremely successful. A grunt as we passed each other in the hallway or on the stairs was his warmest greeting. My mealtimes had eventually been rearranged to keep us apart. I had tea at 4.30 after school and supper at 8 in my room.

My room – a room of my very own – had an oval dressing-table, the base of which had a flouncy skirt in the same material as the pretty chintz curtains, and a matching stool. On the glass top stood a bedside lamp with a blue shade similar in colour to the square of carpet that covered most of the floor. My bed was to the left of the dressing-table, facing the garden, and had a pink embroidered silky bedspread. A dark wooden chest of drawers stood in a recess opposite, next to which was a matching wardrobe. I wondered if anyone could ever own enough clothes to fill the wardrobe and drawers. I was soon to learn that I could, as Mrs Oakes set about making me clothes. Each time I entered this beautiful room I felt delight and wonder that it really belonged to me. I wished my brothers and Anna could see it, but most of all I wished that they could all share it with me. I had more space than the five of us had had at home.

At first I was unhappy at my new school, having started mid-term. However, during a domestic science lesson a girl named Pauline was having difficulties attaining the right consistency for the butter icing we were making for butterfly cakes. She'd used an awful lot of butter and very little icing sugar. Our teacher, Miss Lange, made us beat the icing sugar in the bowls until the butter turned pure white, our hands cramped with the effort.

'Here, let me have a go,' I offered, and added more icing sugar until Pauline's icing turned from saffron to primrose. There was little I could do to rescue her attempt at a sponge, however; Pauline's cakes looked like two limpets resting on a sandcastle.

'Flight, girl, flight! Butterfly cakes should be light as their name denotes. Light, wings in motion, like the new girl's here! Baperweights, that's what these are, girl, baperweights!' To emphasize the point she dropped poor Pauline's culinary attempts bomp! bomp! bomp! on the table.

I flinched for Pauline and felt guilty that Miss Lange had used the 'new girl's' cakes as an example when there were others as good as mine and better. Pauline's face was flushed from more than the heat of the ovens. She had received two out of ten, a very 'boor' mark, as Miss Lange had told her, and I felt at a loss as to what to say.

'It isn't all your fault,' I told Pauline reassuringly, as we cleaned the oven. 'She uses far too much water. If she says two teaspoons of anything, we should only use one!'

'How's that?' Pauline turned and looked at me for the first time, wondering if the mystery new girl had corden bleu cookery standards.

'Well, haven't you noticed how she spits? It's a "binch" of salt and a "binch" of bicarbonate of soda. "I like to use lots of orange "beel" with my fruit cake, girls." By the time she's mixed her ingredients so much spittle has gone into the mixing bowl you've got double the liquid in the recipe!' Pauline was laughing so much that I continued my mimicry of the poor teacher's speech impediment. 'So don't make any more "baper-weight's or I'll give you another "boor" mark, girl!'

Other girls were beginning to show some curiosity at our laughter – Pauline's laugh was very infectious.

'Berhaps you'd like to share the joke, or clean another cooker?' Miss Lange inquired. 'I'm sure there's another oven . . .'

'No, Miss. Sorry, Miss,' Pauline stifled a giggle.

Outside, as we carried our tins of cakes home, we were joined by two girls, Margaret and Jill. Pauline explained the reason for the laughter and the other girls found it equally funny.

'Is it true you're a fosty?' Jill asked.

'Yes,' I replied. This answer was received with an exchange of looks between the three girls that I knew boded ill for me. I felt that I'd had something in my grasp and with one stupid word had lost it for ever.

'Well, I've got to go this way,' I said. 'I'll see you tomorrow.' I walked away with my head bent, holding back the tears. I knew that there was only one girl, another Margaret, who walked my way home and she usually had to run back to meet her little brother. Suddenly there was a tug on my arm. I jumped, nearly dropping the tin of butterfly cakes. It was Pauline.

'Sorry, I didn't mean to make you jump!'

'You didn't,' I lied.

'Did your mum and dad have you put away, then?'

I shook my head.

'They're not divorced, are they?'

Again I shook my head.

'Oh, no! They're not dead, are they? Are they?' she repeated, holding the sleeve of my school blazer.

This time I nodded.

'You an orphan, then?'

Another mute nod. Wondering what the reaction would be from Pauline and the other girls, what status this would compound, I stood there full of self-pity, not wanting to answer any more of Pauline's questions.

'Oh, God, I can't think of anything in the world that would be worse than being an orphan, honest! If anything happened to my mum and dad, I'd die, straight up I would!' she said dramatically. Tears were in her eyes and she put an arm around my neck. 'Will you be my best friend?'

Her question was a bolt from the blue. 'Do you mean it?' I asked incredulously.

'Yeah, of course I do!' Juggling her satchel and cake tin, she extended her left little finger in a crook towards me, indicating that I should extend my right. Our little fingers intertwined, she shook them three times.

'For life,' she said. 'That's what we do down here when we make best friends.'

'For life,' I repeated, unsure what was expected of me. As no further instruction was issued, we promised to meet at the sweet shop near where she lived at 8.45 the next morning.

I flew home with my Home & Colonial tin, propelled by the butterfly cakes it contained. I had a best friend for life (and, indeed, Pauline remained my best friend at that school until I left). I realized I was late and Mums would be cross, but even if she were, it wouldn't be so bad – I had a best friend and I wanted the whole world to know.

I turned into the garden gate, happier than I'd been for ages. The gooseberry bush was beginning to show its green translucent fruit, and there were clusters of berries on the black- and redcurrant bushes, some green, others turning black and red. I gazed up at the cherry tree, where the red fruits showed in patches, and at the apple tree, with its apples at different sizes and stages of growth. It was truly wonderful! I paused at the straw-berry bed, the leaves around the green fruit flattened to the ground as though Mums had cut round them with her pinking shears. The flower borders were a riot of colour, the roses blooming. Mums had been surprised when I'd told her the name of a pale yellow rose; it was 'Peace'. Mummy had shown it to me and told me it was her favourite flower. I would ask Mums if Pauline could come and see the garden, and I'd show her my mother's favourite rose, the bird table Dads had built and all the other beautiful things there.

I heard Blimp, the golden Labrador, scratching at the kitchen door and it opened just as I was about to run to let him out. I'd been afraid of him when I first came here, but now he and I were good friends.

'Have you only just got in?' Mums's voice was sharp.

'Yes, sorry I'm late. I was talking to my best friend.' This vital piece of information was lost on Mums.

'I expected you to have laid the table and washed the lettuce as I asked. After all, ducks, I did leave you a note. I had to go back up the town – I'd left the tomatoes and cucumber in Haynes's. I'd have thought you'd have liked topping and tailing the strawberries, bit more exciting than doing the radishes. Then I got the double cream for 'em. Still, if you want something done, do it yourself, Kath.' She sniffed an air of disapproval. I gazed in amazement at the colander full of plump red strawberries, twice the size of the ones I'd seen on the barrows in London, and handed Mums back the note.

'What good'll that do now?' she asked indignantly.

'Oh, sorry. Shall I do the strawberries now?' I asked hopefully.

'You, young lady, will wash that lettuce an' top and tail the radishes . . . first,' she added reluctantly.

I washed the strawberries as she showed me, taking off their stalks and paring the bottoms, which were a bit tough.

'I got eight for my butterfly cakes today, Mm,' I informed her.

2

I lay awake as the evening sun shone through the curtains, wondering if Anna and my brothers were missing me. My birthday had been in the early spring and there had been no cards from any of them.

The loneliest nights of my life had been spent in this beautiful room, where I would often cry myself to sleep. I missed my mother, my grandmother and the others so–. I didn't even have a photograph of any of them. Remembering my cat, Prowler, brought me grief too. I even missed my father, who had made me take Prowler to be destroyed and bring back his death certificate from the PDSA; my father, who had told me that I was responsible for my mother's death.

It had been during the autumn – pomegranate time – after Ruth Ellis had been hanged that Mummy was taken back into hospital for another operation on her brain. This time the surgeons had taken the bone from the right side of her head. We had been frightened when Mummy came home from hospital because not only had they shaved off all her hair again, but they had also made what Mummy called her 'ski-slope', and you could see her brain beating just like the soft spot on Anna's head. She started to have epileptic fits too. The first was when she was feeding Anna. I thought she was dying as the baby rolled from her breast – I managed to catch her just before she fell to the floor. We were the only three in the house. As Mummy's body twitched and her eyes rolled back to show their whites, her mouth foaming, I ran screaming from the flat with Anna under my arm like a rag doll.

As my mother's hair grew again into bubbly black curls, her ski-slope also began to grow.

The last time my mother had walked or seen anything was one evening the following spring when she had taken me to see *Footsteps in the Fog*, starring Jean Simmons and Stewart Granger. The significance of that title was to remain with me for ever: as we walked home from the cinema, my mother's sight was gradually fading. It was a great effort for her, and as soon as we reached our flat I got her on to the bed-settee. Her last footsteps. She told me to put on the light, but it was on . . .

By July Mummy could no longer speak, and her diet consisted of Bengers' Food, Brand's Essence of Beef, boiled water and injections. The doctor and nurse called several times a day now. On one of those stifling hot days I reached across her to where her feeder beaker stood on the window-sill and knocked her head with my elbow. Mummy flinched. I tried to tell the nurse what had happened, but she didn't seem to think it important; she was more concerned that I leave the room. I think she was distressed that I should see my mother like this. She was a lovely lady, Mummy's nurse.

That afternoon I collected Anna from the day nursery. I was wearing a new straw school hat, and took this to be the reason for the neighbours' smiles as I carried Anna on one hip, my school satchel balancing her weight on the other. As I reached the Mansions, Maggie, the pretty young lady who lived across the road, beckoned me over. I noticed that the old gold curtains in the front room, where my mother's bed was, were drawn, but it was a hot afternoon and the sun strong.

'Go in to see your daddy, darling. Let me take Anna. Be quick now.'

Anna was snatched from my grasp and I dropped my satchel by Maggie's fence. Running into the hallway of the Mansions, I saw my father was crying.

'Oh, darlin', come quickly, come with Daddy.' He was half dragging me towards the front room, pulling me close to him and down beside the bed. 'She's gone, darlin'. Yer mammy's dead,' he sobbed.

No, God, no! This was a nightmare, these were more of his lies. I looked down to where my mother lay, her head slightly to one side, eyes partly open, her mouth pulled down to one side in a sickly leer. Thick white slime covered her mouth, and her tongue was protruding slightly.

'Come darlin', kiss yer Mammy.'

'No, no!' I recoiled in horror.

'Kiss yer Mammy!' He grasped the back of my neck. The gold curtains gave her a yellow pallor. I kissed the sticky white glue of her lips, glue that was still warm. The smell, the woody, acrid smell of death. No! no! this wasn't my mother, this was a monster. 'Oh, Mummy,' my soul seemed to scream silently, 'you were beautiful – where are you?'

'Now we'll say a Hail Mary, sure we will.'

'Hail Mary, full of grace, blessed art thou amongst women and blessed is the fruit of thy . . .'

A 'cic-cic-cic' sound came from my mother's throat. I got up and ran from the room, urine trickling warm down my legs. I passed the priest in the hall and ran and ran to my brother's school.

That night Anna and I stayed in Maggie's prefab. The boys were with other neighbours. I looked out of the window across to where my mother lay. Orange candles were flickering and I could see my father's silhouette walking to and fro.

After my mother's elaborate funeral had taken place Daddy became very kind to us all for a while. One night I confessed to him about knocking her head that terrible day. My father took me in his arms and reassured me, telling me Mummy was going to die anyway, and I mustn't be frettin' so over such a thing. It was some time later that he showed me what he said was a pathologist's report, which declared that my mother's death had been caused by a blow on the head. My guilt and horror knew no bounds, and thereafter my father pursued a campaign of terror.

He'd begun to drink heavily and rely more and more on morphine, which we knew put him in a good mood. His visits to a spiritualist and his involvement with the occult led to him bringing me home all sorts of messages of forgiveness from my mother. At other times he would wake me, whispering 'murderer.' He would creep up behind me when I was getting a bucket of coal from the coal-shed and whisper it. Sometimes he would come in and whisper it in my ear when I lay in bed trying to get Anna off to sleep. Anna would chuckle, thinking Daddy was playing a game. No one could ever say that chilling word with more menace.

I believed, as he now clearly did, that I had indeed murdered my mother. At times I seriously thought about giving myself up, only to be terrified at the thought of leaving my brothers and sisters. I wondered if there were a children's prison inside Holloway.

Now, as I lay in bed, I wondered what Pauline would think if she knew the truth about my mother's death. My thoughts strayed to my mother's words: 'there are different types of killing ...' I had never even dreamed of killing anyone, but had I secretly wanted to kill the monster my mother had become in order to resurrect my real mummy? I tried to banish this thought by covering my head with the crisp white sheet. The orange candle glowed ... Miss Lange's orange 'beel', the reason that I now had my best friend, Pauline; orange peel burning under a candle's flame, burning skin to black ash and my best friend cremated in the oven of my guilt.

I often wondered if Miss Crowley, my Child Care Officer, knew what had happened that July morning and had told Mr and Mrs Oakes during one of their murmured conversations when she called to see me. They would usually have a cup of tea and I'd be asked if I had any homework, as they'd like 'a little word'. Later, I would be called down to see Miss Crowley on my own. She would inquire how I was settling down and always told me what a lucky girl I was. How was I getting on at school? 'Splendid, keep it up Caroline.' There was never any variation. I would then automatically return to my bedroom, until Mr or Mrs Oakes called me downstairs again. The three of us would see Miss Crowley to the door and wave as she climbed into her Morris Minor and drove off, always crashing the gears. The ritual would be over for another month and I'd breathe a sigh of relief as the car bunny-hopped out of sight.

3

It was a warm summer evening towards the end of July, the first anniversary of my mother's death. My eyes were sore and prickling, my nose and mouth felt swollen, my breath came in hot gasps as I lay in bed. Mr Oakes came into my room.

'What's the matter, luv?' he asked, stroking my damp hair.

'I mm ... miss my mummy and the boys and the baby,' I sobbed.

'Oh, sweetheart,' he said, cradling me in his arms and gently gathering me up to lay my head on his chest. 'There, there, I know, I know. No, I don't of course, but I'll try to understand. I'll get Mums to come up with some Horlicks and sit with you, OK?' Kissing the top of my head, he left the bedroom.

Mrs Oakes appeared with a cup of Horlicks. 'Come on, luvvy, be a brave girl. Eh! I saw a smashing pattern for a frock in Soames' today. We'll make it in pink-and-white gingham, eh? Now then, finished?' She took the half-full cup of creamy beverage away. 'Now you get some sleep. God luv a duck, you'll upset everyone if you carry on like this. I've said it before and I'll say it again, time heals everything. Yes it does, you'll see. Night, night, ducks.'

'Night, night,' I managed to whisper. Time healed.

This expression puzzled me. How could time heal what had been taken away for ever?

A cold rainy night in August. Mrs Oakes had promised that Pauline could come to tea on Saturday and now, once more, it seemed that she couldn't. Mr and Mrs Knightley, the Oakeses' best friends, were coming over with their holiday snaps, and Mrs Oakes wasn't going to put them off for a friend of mine, not a girl from 'market people' as she described them. I'd been to tea three times at Pauline's house during the summer holidays, and her mum and dad and big sister Deirdre were lovely. Pauline's parents ran a fruit and vegetable stall in the market and were very kind and friendly. I didn't know how I was going to tell Pauline that the tea invitation had been cancelled again.

I lay in bed, my fear of losing Pauline's friendship over this latest development growing by the minute. She'd broken our friendship for two days when it had happened the second time; it could be for ever if I had to tell her a third time. I tried to think up a weighty enough excuse.

Rain stabbed at my bedroom window and tears fell soft and warm down my cheeks. Mummy had never broken a promise, but Mrs Oakes wasn't like my mother. The thought of how my mother would have liked Pauline caused further agony and I buried my face in my pillow to stifle the sobs.

Mr Oakes came into my bedroom. "'Ello, not more tears, luvvy? Missing them all again, are you? It's only natural. I expect the holidays aren't helping either, eh? I expect you did lots of things together, you and your brothers, eh?' This brought on a fresh outbreak of tears

26

and once again he lifted my head up off the pillow, massaging the back of my neck and my upper arms. His teeth were clenched just as they were when he played with Blimp, patting the dog's stomach when it rolled over and muttering 'Whose my lovely boy then? Good boy, good boy' as the dog nuzzled up to him, licking his face.

I was wearing baby-doll pyjamas, white with red hearts, which Mrs Oakes had made for me. Mr Oakes was still gently stroking my arms. His breathing quickened and I thought he was getting up to leave. Suddenly one of his hands clutched at my tender, growing breasts, and the pain made me scream out. Gently he covered my mouth with his hand and released his grip on my breast, which felt like it was burning. Then he got up and left the room. How long I lay there, rigid in the darkness, I don't know. I didn't cry, I just lay as still as I could. At last sleep overcame me.

A hand was shaking me, a hand from the past. My first thought was that my father had come back to whisper that terrifying word . . . murderer.

'Caroline, Caroline, sweetheart, it's me, Dads. Wake up!'

I lay with my eyes tightly closed. I didn't want to wake up ever!

'I know you're awake.' Silence. Again he shook my arm and called my name.

'Oh! Am I late?' I rubbed my eyes. Early light penetrated the curtains and the birds were beginning their song to the world.

He stood over me in his striped pyjamas. His dishevelled grey hair looked like a thin Brillo pad and he was pushing his glasses up and down on the bridge of his nose, which was, I later discovered, a sign of agitation or annoyance. Putting his fingers to his lips, he whispered, 'It's early. Would you like some Ribena?'

I nodded. It meant he would leave me alone for a few minutes to collect my thoughts. What did I feel? Fear? Guilt? Had I imagined the whole thing? This experience was new to me, guilt and fear habitual. I looked down the scooped neck of the pyjama top. Aware of a bruising ache, I now saw that my right breast was as red as the blood orange Pauline's dad had shown me. One gentle probe at the tender flesh nearly made me cry out. No, it wasn't a dream; it was horribly, terribly real.

There was a shuffle as the door opened. I quickly put my arms down by my sides.

'Sit up, sweetheart.' I did as I was told and accepted the glass of hot Ribena with thanks. This luxurious new beverage now had no more taste than coloured water. As I sipped it, Mr Oakes sat at the foot of my bed, stubby hands plucking at the grizzled grey hair.

'Would you like to go to Bognor this weekend? You like the seaside, don't you, sweetheart?'

'We can't. Mr and Mrs Knightley are coming. That's why Pauline can't come to tea.' I began to tremble.

'Well, I don't see why we can't go on Sunday. We could take your friend too. You'd like that, wouldn't you?'

I nodded vigorously and the pale burgundy drink spilt on to the white sheet.

'Oh, I'm sorry, sorry!' I cried.

'Stay there, I'll get a cloth. Blackcurrant stains, and we don't want Mums to know. It'll be our little secret.'

The ambiguity of his words and the conspiratorial wink were not lost on me. I heard him running a tap in the bathroom next door. I jumped out of bed and pulled on a skirt and cardigan over my pyjamas. Sitting on the dressing-table stool, I heard him behind me attending to the sheet, sponging the stain that would annoy Mums. I sipped the now cool blackcurrant drink in silence. Could he wipe away the stain he had left on my body? And which one would annoy Mums most? I sat there feeling confused, guilty and bewildered.

'Time to get Mums her tea and let Blimp out, sweetheart. And Gordon will be wanting his cup of Nescafé. Finish that drop of Ribena, there's a good girl, and I'll take your glass. Bless my boots, that sheet's nearly dry; no one would ever know. I'll make somebody a good wife one day, eh? eh?' Tousling my hair, he shuffled out of the room, chuckling quietly at his little joke.

As soon as he had gone I drew the curtains wide. Outside on the bird table the blue tits were hovering around, waiting for their breakfast. Last night's rain had left the flower borders, the roses and the lawn winking like a million diamond chips as the sun began its ascent. The back door opened and Blimp bounded down the garden path. This garden, which had been my Eden, would never be the same for me. The fruits that it bore, the joy in picking them, had been stolen from me.

Suddenly I wanted my father. Yes, he'd beaten me both physically and psychologically, but I knew, I knew more than anything, that he would never never have allowed this man, this stranger whom I was to call 'Dads', to have done this to me. I threw myself on the bed and called to him, 'Daddy, Daddy come back, come back to me!'

'Aren't you up yet, ducks?' Mrs Oakes's voice penetrated my misery.

'Yes, I won't be long, Mm.' I tried to make my voice sound as normal as possible. I sat up swiftly and pulled on a clean pair of socks. Then I grabbed a clean vest and pants from the chest of drawers, and a blue striped blouse Mums had recently made me, and took them all into the bathroom.

The bathroom smelled of Gibbs S.R. Toothpaste, Palmolive soap and fragrant fern bath salts. I looked in the mirror of the bathroom cabinet. My face was blotchy, my eyes puffy and bloodshot. I ran the cold tap and splashed my face with cold water again and again, the freezing water assaulting my cheeks and eyes. I cleaned my teeth and gently dried my face. A look in the mirror told me that the blotching on my face was worse. The soreness in my right breast forced me to look again at the injury I had received. I gasped as the pure natural light of the bathroom revealed a million pinpricks of blood surrounding the pink nipple, and faint marks the colour of a thundercloud on the small white growing breast.

As I reached up to open the cabinet door, more tears began to mist my eyes, making my throat ache. I found a roll of cotton wool wrapped in dark-blue paper and a bottle of witch-hazel. Gingerly, I dabbed at my face and my breast with a saturated pad of cotton wool. Screwing the top back on the bottle and replacing the roll of cotton wool, my eyes came to rest on a large bottle of aspirin. It was the second time I had realized that I could take my own life. This knowledge filled me with awe and a perverse elation. I had the power to decide whether to live or die and no one could take that from me. I was twelve years old and could make the greatest choice there was.

An abrupt knocking on the bathroom door made me jump.

'How much longer are you gonna be in there?' It was Gordon.

'Coming out now,' I called, throwing the pad of cotton wool down the toilet and pulling the chain. My hands shook as I fumbled to do up the buttons on my blouse. It was then I realized I was still holding the bottle of Allen & Hanbury's 100 Aspirin B.P. tightly in my left hand. Slowly I replaced the bottle in the cabinet and closed the door.

''Bout bloody time!' Gordon spat as I hurried past him.

Downstairs Mums didn't look up as I entered the kitchen. She was dashing around the kitchen like someone in those old 'speeded-up' silent films, except she wasn't silent.

'Come on, ducks, your breakfast's ready and Gordon's really cross. I don't blame him either! You mustn't stay in the bathroom so long. My men have got to have their shaves and things and get to work on time. You may not have noticed, but you're not the only person in this house. Now then, go on into the dining-room, out from under my feet,' she scolded.

It was the first time she'd been really cross with me and I wanted to say I was sorry. This time I couldn't though, and did as I was told, my throat thick, my chest heavy and my right breast feeling as if someone had tried to screw it off.

Mrs Oakes's breakfasts were a fairly formal affair. There were no split shifts in the mornings to avoid Gordon. The dining-room table was spread with a selection of cereals, home-made brown bread and conserves, fresh fruit and tea. Coffee was reserved for Gordon. Mr Oakes was sitting at his usual place, giving Blimp pieces of brown bread and honey. His wife, following behind me, ushered me to my chair, where I sat with my back to the french windows. A dish of brown strands of All-Bran cereal topped with chopped banana was placed in front of me with a thud. I whispered my thanks.

'Are you going to eat it or stare at it? Make up your mind.' Mrs Oakes was glowering at me. 'What's the matter? You been cryin' again?'

'I had a bad nightmare.' It took some time to find my voice and when I did, it seemed to come out in a low-pitched growl.

'That's that Welsh rarebit you had for tea last night, my girl. No more cheese for you near bedtime.'

Mr Oakes scraped back his chair noisily. I didn't look up.

'Got to be going, Mums. Another day, another dollar, eh? Hadn't you better give our Gordon a shout?'

'Not likely. He's like a bear with a sore head this morning. I can't say I blame him, mind,' Mrs Oakes sniffed.

'Bye, luvvy,' Mr Oakes said, tapping me on the head as I chewed and chewed on the stringy brown strands, which refused to pass my tonsils.

Mrs Oakes got up to see him to the door. I could hear Gordon descending the stairs. There was a muffled exchange between parents and son while I quickly gave Blimp as much of my cereal as I could. Then I collected most of the used crockery and took it to the kitchen to avoid any further physical contact with Gordon. The Oakeses were still speaking in low tones as I returned to collect some more dishes. Closing the kitchen door on

32

them, I began to tackle the washing-up. I worked so swiftly that I giggled at the thought that Mrs Oakes and I could be in the same old film. I would be the girl tied to the railway track, but I didn't want the hero to untie me just as the train was looming; I wanted to lie on the track and be crushed, as Mr Oakes had crushed me with his hand last night. I wouldn't have minded a train; I did mind Mr Oakes. I was wiping down the brown crumbs that were on the pulled-down leaf of the kitchen cabinet.

'Gordon's coffee . . . "I like coffee, I like tea, I like the Java Jive and it likes me . . ."' Gordon's mother, I was discovering, had a song for almost anything. 'S'cuse, luv,' she murmured as she took the cup of milky coffee into the dining-room, praising me for clearing away and washing the breakfast dishes. I wondered what had been said on the doorstep to bring about her good mood.

I heard Gordon leave. Mrs Oakes came into the kitchen with his breakfast dishes and the jars of conserve. I took the dishes from her and washed them.

'Dads says we should take you down to Bognor this Sunday and you can bring your friend. Won't that be nice? I'll phone her mother if she's on the phone.'

'Yes, I'll look it up in the book,' I answered eagerly.

Later that evening Mrs Oakes spoke to Pauline's mother on the phone. 'She sounds very nice and she's ever so grateful, I said we'll collect – Patricia, is it? – at 8.30 on Sunday morning.'

'Pauline. Her name's Pauline,' I corrected her. I couldn't wait to see Pauline to make our plans. The thought of a day at the seaside with her was the most soothing balm anyone could have given me.

It was not to be, however. On Saturday morning

Pauline's mother telephoned to say that Pauline had gastroenteritis and they were waiting for the doctor to call. All the plans we'd made on Thursday vanished before my eyes and I ran upstairs and lay on the bed and cried.

Sunday brought a howling gale, which swept away plans for going anywhere, and I spent my first afternoon of baking under Mrs Oakes's supervision. This was a routine that would establish itself for most of my Sunday afternoons.

The school term began two weeks later and I had never been so glad to see that old red-brick Victorian building.

4

One of my chores was to prepare the vegetables each morning for the evening meal, and I was happy to do this. This morning, Mrs Oakes had left the colander with the exact amount of vegetables required. I peeled the carrots, onions and potatoes, and put a crust of bread in the potato water to prevent them discolouring as Mums had taught me. The onions were immersed in their salt water and I was shelling the peas when I heard raised voices coming from the dining-room.

'You will do as I say and sit there, Gor–don! And I don't mean maybe!'

I knew it meant trouble when Mrs Oakes called her son 'Gor–don' and ended with 'and I don't mean maybe!' The kitchen door flew open.

'If it's not tears it's tantrums, tantrums and bloody tears. Look at that! A whole pot of bloody tea wasted!' She pushed me aside and emptied a half-full pot of tea down the sink. Filling the kettle, she moved my four saucepans to the open flap of the kitchen cabinet with four deliberate bangs.

'Where's your newspaper for those peelin's?' she demanded.

'I'll go and get . . .'

'I've told you before: prepare, pre–pare! Here!' she waved two sheets of the *Daily Herald* at me.

'Thank you,' I muttered, and proceeded to make a neat package of the peelings and pea shucks. I knew Mr Oakes would retrieve them from the dustbin and put them on his compost heap later.

'And another thing, young lady – you'll have to be a bit more careful with your hygiene!'

'I don't know what ... I always wash and ...' I stammered.

'P'raps so, but you smell under your arms! When Mr and Mrs Knightley was here on Tuesday, you could have knocked us all down with a feather. It's not nice for us, you know. Gordon and Dads were very embarrassed. I mean, we couldn't even open the french doors 'cos it was raining cats and dogs,' she went on relentlessly. 'I'll get you some day-o-dor-ant today,' she snorted. 'After all, Mr Knightley is a policeman,' she concluded, as if underarm odour were punishable by law!

I remembered, oh God, I remembered! The heat of the room, the five of them sipping sherry and me Ribena, while on the television *What's My Line* panellists Lady Isabel Barnet and Barbara Kelly, their eyes covered by fancy black masks, were questioning a celebrity who was doing her best to disguise her voice and be evasive. I'd sat there, my armpits damp and smelling not unlike the vegetables I'd recently stripped of their skins. The memory filled me with shame; my cheeks burned, I wanted to run away, I wanted to die, 100 aspirins' worth, and I would savour every one of them!

When I returned home from school that afternoon there was a Timothy White's & Taylor's bag on the dining-table with a tube of Mum deodorant and a red tin of Coty's L'Aimant talcum powder. From that day on I would rather be without toothpaste than deodorant or talc. (My own first request for 'Mum day-o-dor-ant' in Timothy White's was greeted with perplexity by the helpful young assistant, who – having established I wasn't chanting in Latin – eventually produced the Mum deodorant triumphantly. The brutality of Mrs Oakes's words was to remain with me for ever. The subject was never referred to again – proof, I supposed, that the product actually worked successfully. Soon afterwards I got a newspaper round and banished BO for ever.)

It was the middle of October. The pale green floral cotton curtains that had hung at the french windows had to be replaced by heavy brown velvet ones. Mr Oakes and Gordon went through the annual routine of changing the curtains while Mrs Oakes fussed about how I should assist her in folding the cotton ones for the dry-cleaners. We placed them to her satisfaction into the Sketchley Cleaners bag. I was to take them in on Saturday morning.

Mr and Mrs Knightley were coming that evening and because I'd been admonished several times for disappearing to my room whenever any of the Oakeses' friends called, I now waited it out, said good evening and then asked very politely if I could be excused, as I had homework to do and the genuine excuse of having to get up early to do my paper round. The Knightleys were my biggest dread and I found myself stammering and stumbling over my excuses, my cheeks burning and the perspiration from my palms flowing freely. The Knightleys were always very nice to me. She proffered a cheek, which I would peck, and he always gave my wet hand a squeeze. Once in the safety of the upper part of the

37

house I would sniff at the palms of my hands, relieved that I hadn't contracted 'palm odour'. I eventually invested in some Nulon hand cream – I needed to safeguard myself at all costs!

In the bathroom I would scrub myself from top to toe with Palmolive soap, spread the sticky Mum under my arms, powder my body, clean my teeth and jump into bed. I'd once heard Gordon exclaim, 'Christ! She smells like a Drury Lane whore' as he went into the bathroom after my ablutions. This made me get up again after I'd heard him go downstairs and use additional odour deterrents!

The night of the 'changing of the curtains', as I came to call it, would bring a change that would remain until I left that house. It was a cold night and I'd finished another boring essay on the Industrial Revolution. Especially at this time of the year my thoughts turned to my family. The official starting date for making our guys and securing our pitches was 10 October. For the next ten days our guys were a secret, although appeals for a pair of trousers or additional newspaper for stuffing them would be attended to before the deadline of 20 October. On that date our artistic prowess would be assessed, and no one was allowed to alter their guys in any way.

I wondered now if the boys had made their guy and found a good pitch. I wondered about Anna too. Would they all be missing me as I missed them? I would have given anything in the world for a chance to see them, and my mother, father and grandmother. I tried to remember their voices and how they'd sounded, but I couldn't. I remembered their faces – my mother's before she became sick. My heart jumped as I remembered my father's accusation. I tried to use a mental trip-switch to disconnect that memory, but it seldom worked once it had stolen into my thoughts.

The newsagent where I worked was only just getting in its stocks of Benwell's fireworks. I hadn't seen a single guy sitting in an old push-chair or wooden cart. A tray of poppies for Remembrance Day stood on the counter with a plaque bearing the inscription: 'With the going down of the sun and the rising of the moon, we will remember them.' I had read it and cried, realizing that that was all I would ever be able to do – remember them.

I had brought three things from home, which I kept on a shelf underneath the frilly dressing-table skirt in a big chocolate box that Mrs Oakes had given me. One was a pink chiffon scarf that had belonged to my mother, the flimsy material shredding, so often had I held it to my face. Inhaling the smell of Evening in Paris perfume and of her, my constant comforter, I could close my eyes and make believe she was with me. In an envelope there was a lock of her hair. My father had given us each a curl of the black silk. When I had shown it to Mrs Oakes, she had said it was morbid for a child to have such a thing. I looked at the coarse white hair she was always having to have permed and set at the hairdressers and thought she might be jealous. My third treasure was a Mabel Lucie Attwell annual. Inside my mother had written 'To my darling Caroline, on this your 7th birthday, loving you now and always, Mummy'. The latter just fitted into the bottom of the enormous chocolate box, which had a lid with a yellow satin ribbon across the right-hand corner and a picture of three grey furry kittens sitting in a basket.

I was putting back the book in the base of the chocolate box when the door to my bedroom opened. Hastily, I put in the scarf and envelope and replaced the kitten lid. I had heard the Knightleys leave about half an hour earlier and had been so lost in my reverie that I hadn't heard any noise from downstairs or on the stairs. I had already had my night-time drink of Horlicks, so it was with some surprise that I saw Mr Oakes standing there holding a hot cup of Ovaltine with two chocolate biscuits melting against it. Swiftly, guiltily, I pushed the box under my bed.

"'Ello, sweetheart. What you up to, eh? I saw your light on and thought you couldn't sleep or was upset or something, so I brought you up a nice hot drink and some Cadbury's Shortcakes. I spoil you, don't I, don't I, eh? Not upset then, luvvy? Well, that's something.' He placed the cup and saucer on the glass top of the dressing-table.

'Thank you very much.' My arms crossed themselves over my chest and I hugged myself, hands tense under my arms. I was wearing yellow winceyette pyjamas, which Mrs Oakes had helped me to make. They had the same scooped neck as the baby-doll ones and she'd shown me how to make and add the long sleeves. The trousers were knee-length, and I'd trimmed them and the scooped neck with white lace. They were the first things I'd ever made on my own, though closely supervised, and I'd been very proud. Mrs Oakes hadn't said anything to me, but she must have been proud too, because she had shown them to Miss Crowley.

I felt a surge of panic. Since my encounter with Mr Oakes back in the summer I'd been self-conscious about my, albeit thin, body, and my breasts had grown quite a bit. Mrs Oakes still hadn't given her approval for a 'braziah', as she called it, telling me that I still had only 'bee-stings'. Most of the girls in school had bras, but one outburst from me had resulted in 'I buy for you and I'm happy to do so, but I'm not spending money on luxuries you don't need, my girl, and I don't mean maybe . . .' and ended any further entreaties.

I crawled into bed and Mr Oakes handed me the cup of Ovaltine, its sides spattered with globules of melted chocolate. As I tried to peel one of the sticky biscuits from the side of the cup we both laughed at the gooey mess on my fingers.

'You mucky pup, I'll go and get a face-cloth from the bathroom. Won't be a minute!'

Just going to the bathroom to get a sponge, blackcurrant stains you know, Mums would be cross. There, it's all gone, no one would ever know! Blackcurrant stains, redcurrant juice – speckled blood, bruises . . .

Coming back from the bathroom armed with a face-cloth and towel, Mr Oakes replaced the cup and saucer on the dressing-table. 'Can I use a piece of this?' He picked up a sheet of paper on which I had written my essay outline. I nodded my head and he put the biscuits on the paper. 'This'll teach me to do things properly, or prepare, as Mums always says, and get a tea plate, eh? We'll be for it if she sees that cup, won't we, eh?'

The face-cloth was cold as, one by one, he wiped my fingers, slowly, methodically, drying each one painstakingly with the towel. 'You've got lovely long fingers. P'raps we should get you piano lessons. Would you like that?' Again I nodded.

'C'mon, you silly sausage, you've got some on your chin.' Pulling my face towards him, he began to wipe my chin, then my throat. The cloth was icy. I began to push his hands away frantically. 'Little tiger,' he rasped, his breath coming in short gasps. His teeth, no longer clenched, were grinding now. I was pushing him away with all my strength, calling for help. His hands flew under my pyjama top, cold air, cold spectacles, hot lips sucking at my breasts as I'd watched Anna do to my mother. My hands tore at the wire-wool hair. His hand was savagely pulling at my pyjama bottoms, elastic surrendering as he groped over my stomach towards my 'private parts', as his wife called them. I was pushing at his head when I felt something hard above the fleshy ear. Pulling upwards on it, I heard a snap. Suddenly it was all over, as if the snap had been a shot from a gun. He stood up in a daze. His glasses had fallen on to the bed and I was holding the side-piece of the spectacles in my hand.

I'd never seen him without his glasses before. He looked strange, a strange stranger.

'I'm telling Mums ... I'm telling the police ... I'm ...' Uncontrollable shaking overcame me. Suddenly he was coming towards me again.

'My glasses ...' I pushed the broken bar of his glasses at his hand. He grasped it and was gone.

The cup of Ovaltine stood on the dressing-table, the two biscuits on the white sheet of essay paper next to it. I was half lying, half sitting my head and neck at a tortuous angle. My bare back was pressed against the cold wall, but, surprisingly, the front of my pyjamas still covered my breasts. How long had it taken? Minutes? Seconds? It had seemed to go on for hours.

I don't know how long I lay there. Suddenly I heard the front door close. I got up and pulled on my school jumper and my socks. I heard Gordon and his mother talking.

'Well, I think it's a snip, luvvy, and I'm sure Dads will like the idea. I could make him a jumper in a weekend. You can't go wrong with something one of the Knightley family is selling. Marion's sister's a gem, letting it go at that price. Still, your father will have the last word. We could make a good bit of profit, especially with winter nearly upon us. Where is he anyway? He's left the lights on. That's not like him!'

I switched off the bedside lamp as I heard Mrs Oakes coming up the stairs. 'Artie! Artie! Oh, Artie, it's marvellous, we'd be stupid not to buy at that price. The profit we could make! I'm not kidding, even our Gordon's . . . What's the matter? What you laying in the dark for? Well, why didn't you say? I wouldn't have gone if I'd known. Can I get you something, luvvy?'

I sat in the dark, shivering. I pulled the eiderdown round me, a fortress of feathers. I heard Gordon going into the bathroom whistling 'Singin' the Blues'. I heard him urinate and then begin brushing his teeth. He always made such disgusting sounds when he cleaned his teeth. God, how I hated him! His curly grey hair was so thin it looked as if someone had scattered a few grey grasses on pink barren land. The pink scalp shone through the sparse curls. He had a long face and I'd never really seen his eyes, as he kept them averted. He had quite a nice nose, full red lips and brilliant white teeth, which he seemed to keep that way with his strange, noisy, nauseating ritual in the bathroom. He was of slight build, like his father, but was facially more like his mother.

Although now very plump, Mrs Oakes was taller than both 'her men'. She had beautiful large blue eyes with thick dark lashes, a pretty, pert nose and the full red mouth inherited by her son. Her front teeth protruded slightly, but she was a pretty woman with a surprisingly light, youthful carriage, in sharp contrast to her son's slight stoop and sluggish movement. If her hair weren't so white, and permed like an old lady's, I thought she would probably look as young as Gordon.

I now heard Gordon slope off to his bedroom and close the door. Still I stayed sitting in the dark, the eiderdown engulfing me. I could hear Mrs Oakes in the next room murmuring to her husband. Eventually everything in the house was silent. Still I sat there . . . perhaps he was waiting for her to go to sleep. As soon as he opened the door to my bedroom I knew what I was going to do: I would scream the house down, and I didn't care if they put me in Dr Barnardo's; it would be better there. Even if they put me in the children's prison at Holloway, at least I'd have wardresses. I'd seen them walking to and from the prison all my life, and some of them were very pretty. Remembering Holloway, I thought of Mummy and called out in the darkness. If there were another life after this one, why wasn't she helping me now? She knew I hadn't meant to kill her!

5

I awoke. It was dark and freezing. I wondered what I was doing in my pyjama bottoms, with my school jumper and socks on. Suddenly I remembered. My neck was stiff and my body sore and aching. The clock said 5.15. In three hours I would be away from here for ever. Then I noticed that the cup, saucer and biscuits had gone. An old terror gripped me. A pulse in the base of my spine began to beat the painful tattoo I had experienced during my father's reign of terror. *He* had been in while I had been asleep. Apart from taking the cup, saucer and biscuits, what else had he done? My imagination began to run riot and, panic-stricken with the need to get out of this house, I switched on the lamp, got a blouse and jumper from the drawer, and took a pair of trousers and my moccasin shoes from the wardrobe.

Gingerly, I took off my school jumper and pyjama top. I was shivering from fear and the coldness of the room, but I had to see what he had done to me this time. Once again my growing breasts were pinpricked with blood, both of them this time, and red bruising tinged with blue was already forming a pattern over them and my chest and sternum. Rolling down the pyjama bottoms I saw more bruising over my hips and a raised white weal slashed like a half moon across my stomach.

I cannot remember feeling any physical pain, only the cold, and seeing my pretty lace-trimmed vest white and innocent against the ugliness of my wounds. Now a primeval cry escaped from my throat and I called out to my father and mother. 'Mummy, Daddy, come back! Please, please, don't leave me here. Daddy, please, Daddy!' I rocked to and fro, but they were not listening and I knew that I was completely alone.

At last I dressed and lay on my bed. I had about seventeen shillings saved and I would go to see Miss Crowley. I wondered where I'd be this time tomorrow. I'd miss Pauline and Blimp and Mrs Oakes too. Perhaps if she'd let me have a bra it would have stopped him. Perhaps that's why people wore them – to keep predators like him away.

Someone flushed the toilet and I quickly scrambled back into bed, covering my head with the sheet. Footsteps paused outside my door and I knew he would come in. I held my breath and thought my heart would stop beating. There was a padding of feet now, and I heard Gordon's door close. I let out a long sigh of relief and switched the lamp off. The clock said five past six. I would get up at half past and pack my things. I'd already put my money into the red purse I'd been given for my birthday.

'Come on ducks, wakey, wakey. There's people out there waiting for you to bring them the news of the day.' Mrs Oakes's steel curlers littered her white hair, making her head look like a twirl of tinsel.

'I'm not going ...' I began. I wanted to say I wasn't going anywhere except with Miss Crowley, but looking at Mrs Oakes's large blue eyes, which had flickered from annoyance to concern, my courage failed me.

46

'You ill? You been sick?' I could only nod tearfully. 'Must've been those fish cakes last night. That's you and Dads both down with the food poisoning. I'll see that Fletcher – the price he charges for his cod too!' She put a cool hand on my forehead. 'Umm ... got a temperature an' all!' she pronounced, shaking her head, which gave off a tinny rattle. 'I'll go and phone the newsagent's. Dads will 'ave to stop home an' all, he's not well neither.' My heart gave a lurch but she countered with, 'I won't be going in to Murray's, not with you two to look after. Just as well we had the phone put in. Can I get you some water or something? Dads is gonna try a cup of tea but against my advice.'

'Water's fine,' I whispered. Curlers tinkling, she left the room.

I awoke to sharp needles of rain slashing at the window-pane, and raised voices coming from downstairs.

'I wish you wouldn't put all these paper bags and string in these damn drawers, Kathleen. What are all these damn pieces of paper? And a needle! My God, woman!' Mr Oakes's voice, angry with his wife for the first time.

'That's what kitchen drawers are for, Artie, not old glasses. Anyway, I've always told you, pre–pare!'

'You need to prepare if you go on putting bloody needles in them. It's gone down my thumbnail. Damn!'

'Listen, Artie, don't you start swearing at me. Here, get out of my way and my kitchen. You're as blind as a bat!'

'Got 'em!' Mr Oakes shouted triumphantly. 'Sorry, darling, didn't mean to be cross with you!'

'Shush!' The volume was turned up on the wireless

and I could hear John Hanson singing 'One Alone' from *The Desert Song*. John Hanson was not alone, for Mrs Oakes began a duet with him. Later I heard the front door close.

I must have drifted back to sleep. The house was silent when I awoke. I got up, still fully clothed, and crept into the bathroom. Sitting on the edge of the bath, I pulled up my blouse, vest and jumper. The bruises seemed to be a far more livid purple now. If no one was in, I would phone Miss Crowley. I knew her number was in the red book by the telephone in the hall. A knock on the bathroom door made me jump.

'That you, luvvy?'

'Yes, I'll be out now.'

'You been sick again?'

'No,' I answered truthfully and opened the bathroom door.

'Where d'you think you're going dressed like that, eh? You don't look well at all. Go and get those clothes off and your 'jamas on. I'll bring you up a hot-water bottle. Would you like some more water or do you think you could manage a cuppa?'

'I think I can manage some tea.' I managed to smile wanly at her.

She came into the bedroom with a hot-water bottle, cup of tea and a pink fluffy bedjacket that she insisted I put on. Carefully and without any admonishment, she began folding the clothes I'd discarded.

'Lift up.' Gently she plumped up my pillows, tucked me into bed, felt my forehead and handed me my cup of tea. She sat on my bed, smoothing the sheet. 'You'll never guess where Dads is.'

*

Prison? Dead? Squashed under the three wheels of Gordon's bubble car? Lying in the morgue?

I shook my head.

'Work, would you believe? And he was as sick as a dog last night. I phoned Taylor at the newsagent's. He was ever so good, said to tell you to get better quick, he knew you wouldn't 'ave let him down without good reason. Then I phoned Murray's to tell them I wouldn't be in and I'm just gonna phone Dads's office and downstairs he comes. "I'm feeling much better now Kath," he says, "and I'm going in." I didn't like the look of him, mind, and he's broken his glasses. Well, I won't go into how that happened, not while you're so poorly. I've been down the town while you were asleep and taken them into Theales to be mended.

'I went into Fletcher's the fishmonger and gave him a piece of my mind, I can tell you. Told him I'd get the health people in if anything happened to you or Dads. Not strong enough to take it, you're not. Undernourished when you came here you were, Dr Andrews said so. "You're not going to undo all my good work with that girl," I told him, "Fletcher," I told him straight. "How comes you and your Gordon didn't get it then?" he says, cheeky bugger! You and Dads must 'ave had the cakes from the bad cod, and Gordon and me were lucky.

'Another cuppa? I'll get one for myself and keep you company, ducks. If you're no better by morning I'll have to get Dr Andrews in, and I told Fletcher I won't answer for the consequences!' On that note she left the room, my half-full cup of tea in her hand.

Poor old Mr Fletcher, I thought. What had she said

about 'undoing all her good work'? It made me feel like a piece of her knitting that someone had deliberately unravelled. It was still raining, but I felt glad of her company and safe too. She soon came bustling back into the room with two cups of tea on a tray. She handed me mine and sat down on the dressing-table stool to continue her diatribe.

'So Dads has had to go into work in his steel-rimmed glasses. Our Gordon says they make him look like Christie the murderer. That's the one poor Timothy Evans swung for . . . I shouldn't be talking to you about such things. Finished?'

I gave an involuntary shiver as I handed back the cup, still half full.

'You snuggle up in the warm now, luvvy. Perhaps I should give you an aspirin. I'll see if you're old enough on the bottle.'

Oh, I'm old enough, Mrs Oakes. I'm older than you'll ever know. I feel as if I could handle that whole bottle of aspirin and you'd have no more stitches to count on your knitting.

That night Mrs Oakes brought me a bowl of soup, telling me that Dads had had to go bed as he still felt a bit poorly and had taken some sleeping tablets. I was pleased to hear that.

At about ten o'clock that night I had a bad headache and my nose began to bleed. I remembered the nose-bleed sheet I used to keep in the cupboard at home, tearing pieces off whenever my nose bled copiously, as it so often did. Mrs Oakes brought me a cup of Horlicks with an aspirin. She wanted to put a key down my back

50

to stop the bleeding but I was afraid she would see the bruises, so I held her ineffectual swabs of cotton wool to my nose, tipping my head back while the blood coursed down my throat. Eventually the bleeding stopped and when I woke, it was daylight. Downstairs I could hear the signature tune of *Housewives' Choice* on the wireless. I surveyed the bruises, now clearly indigo blue, and the weal across my stomach which resembled a pink rainbow.

I got out of bed and slowly descended the stairs. Mrs Oakes was sitting at the dining-table reading a knitting magazine. She looked up.

'Oh, there you are, luvvy. I hoped you'd sleep on a bit. Do you good.'

'Did you stay home from the shop for me again?' I asked, praying it wasn't for Arthur Oakes.

'Of course I did, ducks. Tell you the truth, you're no trouble and I'm enjoying the break. Well, you're looking a bit better. What would you like, coffee or tea? Manage a bit of toast and honey, could you, eh?'

'Coffee, please, Mm, and toast and honey would be nice.' I smiled at her. She was a good woman and at this moment I wanted to put my arms around her and tell her so. The surge of affection and gratitude I felt for her was overwhelming, but I knew it would be certain folly and that she'd shy away. Instead I told her I'd 'do the cupboards out' later, a job she hated. I knew instinctively that her warm smile and utterance of what a good girl I was were the equivalent of a hug.

Sipping the coffee made with milk (another luxury), and eating toast and honey in a companionable silence, I wondered how Mrs Oakes could possibly be happy with 'her men'. I thought of Arthur Oakes with his thin grizzled hair, long face, slightly bulbous blue eyes and long, sharp pointed nose. He tended to speak out of the corner of his thin mouth, as if he were being economical with those lips for fear of further erosion. He had rather large even teeth, which were slightly yellow. Thin and wiry, he walked very upright, head held high, as if he'd striven to reach the height of his wife for many years.

Was it really only eight months ago that I had looked upon them both as the perfect foster-parents? Mrs Oakes was always making clothes for me and teaching me to cook all sorts of delicious meals. She was strict, but had infinite patience while teaching me to do things. If I'd had a favourite then, it would have been her husband. There'd been his fond teasing and genuine sympathy for my grief at the loss of my beloved family; the outings to the countryside and Bognor Regis in the old Hillman car, with Blimp and me sitting in the back, and picnics fit for a queen. They'd smiled at each other at my delight in the garden and all it held for me. Next spring, he'd promised, I could have my own patch of garden and grow whatever I liked in it. The only blot on the landscape then was Gordon: Gordon, whose one and only love seemed to be his bubble-car, an Issetta he called Izzie-Bon.

'We're buying a knitting machine, luvvy, from Mrs Knightley's sister. She can't get the hang of it. Just think of all the lovely things we'll be able to make, eh?'

'I didn't know you could have knitting machines. Are they like sewing machines?'

'No, not to look at. You either *can* get on with them or you *can't*, and I can. Tell you what, I bet you'll pick it up pretty quick. Look how you took to my old Singer. It's coming tonight, I can't wait to get started. Our

Gordon's picking it up for me in Izzie-Bon after work.'
She rubbed her hands together in anticipation.

'I expect everyone will want you to make them something,' I told her.

'Charity begins at home, my girl, I'll be making for our Gordon, you and Dads to start with. I've learned a hard lesson about making things for strangers. Our Gordon was going to get married two years ago and she jilted him. Antoinette her name was, and she broke my boy's heart, she did.'

There was a silence as her brows creased. She rubbed the side of her face with her fingers as if to erase the memory, her eyes became misty and a tear dwelt on her lower lashes. I wasn't sure what I would do if she started to cry. To my relief she sniffed and directed me to follow her.

'Here, come upstairs, I'll show you something. Leave those.' She indicated the plate and cups and saucers on the table. She led the way to her bedroom. I'd been in there only a few times, to hoover or look in her 'bran-tub', as she called the trunk camouflaged as a dressing-table stool with the same material as the curtains and a cushion on top. Inside the bran-tub was a vast quantity of materials, and I loved it when we went hunting through the 'maze of memories' – every piece of material told a story, Mrs Oakes once said. Now it was the huge oak wardrobe she unlocked, motioning me to sit on the bran-tub.

With much rustling, she withdrew a garment covered in curtaining material with a coat-hanger hook protruding from the top. She removed the cover and revealed something swathed in tissue paper like a mummy from the British Museum. Painstakingly, she unwound the bandages to reveal the most beautiful dress I had ever seen in my life: pure white lace, short full skirt, long sleeves that ended in a 'V' shape over the back of the hands. Tiny teardrop pearls hung on the scooped neck and were scattered over the bodice. The underskirt was made of layers of soft white netting.

'Nottingham lace. I sewed those pearls on by hand; took me weeks.'

'It's the most beautiful dress I've ever seen! You made it all?' I asked incredulously. She nodded.

'Every stitch, and the wedding cake. Three-tier, square. Didn't ice it, mind. Left that to the professionals. I know my limitations.'

'But it's so beautiful, how could she . . .?'

'Oh, she could and she did, luvvy. She did the b–! Bought her a house in Surrey, my Gordon did. Her engagement ring cost over £50. She wasn't brought up too well, if you get my meaning. Oh, the clothes I made her! Course, her people were always hard up, but that didn't worry me and Dads. Gordon was our only one, so we paid up for the wedding, the lot!' She threw her palms downwards in a gesture of despair.

'Wedding invitations had gone out – All Saints, the wedding was to be. Fours weeks before the wedding my Gordon gets a telephone call, at work if you please, from her sister. The wedding was off. Some bloke she'd been out with in her teens had just got back from the army and she was to tell Gordon it wouldn't be fair, as it was this squaddie she really loved. It was more likely his uniform she loved, if she knew the meaning of the word.'

'Did she marry this, er, man from the army?' I inquired.

'Oh yes. Register Office it was. Got a kiddie now, lives out in Monster or some such place in Germany, and I hope she bloody rots there!' Her voice rose as she rewrapped the dress, with much rustling of tissue. 'Dads and me, we worshipped that girl like a daughter, specially Dads. She could do no wrong in his eyes!'

Briefly I wondered what form Dads' worship of this girl had taken. I asked how old she was.

'Ooh, a good bit younger than our Gordon. She was, let's see, about twenty-two. She'll be twenty-four getting on twenty-five now!'

The curtain material was carefully replaced over the swathes of tissue, and Mrs Oakes emitted a loud sigh as she locked the wardrobe door on the beautiful dress. I wondered if she was keeping it in case Antoinette came back from Germany, but I didn't dare ask because Mrs Oakes had said she hoped she'd rot there!

'P'raps now you'll understand why Gordon's a bit grumpy sometimes. He'll never get over her, of course, and there's the shame we've had to bear . . .'

'Oh, poor Gordon. I didn't know. I'm ever so sorry.' And I was.

'Well, it's like I always say, time's the great healer.'

'Yes, you do,' I agreed, thinking that it wasn't working for Gordon or me, but afraid to tell her so. I suddenly felt an empathy with Gordon. We both grieved for the loss of our loved ones, and I really did begin to wonder if Mr Oakes had been instrumental in the girl's running away. After all, I had planned to, and if I'd been old, like twenty-two, and with a sister to tell, I wouldn't be here now.

This reawakened a nagging question in my mind: why had the Oakeses chosen me? I'd spent two trial weekends with them in the beginning while I was await-ing placement. They had only one complaint about me, and that was that I hadn't cleaned out the bath after use. This had had the same effect on me as the deodor-ant issue, and on my second weekend found me using Vim on everything but the ceilings. They'd decided then that I could stay.

'Why did you choose me, Mm?' I asked later that afternoon when I was cleaning out the cupboards with the aforementioned Vim.

'Because we wanted a little girl.' Because they'd lost their daughter-in-law to be? a voice inside me asked, and I felt hurt and jealous over this girl with the French name whom they'd loved so much.

'Miss Crowley said you asked for me specially.' I knew by now that you were chosen if you were lucky, not asked for by name, as Miss Crowley had indicated I had been.

'Well, luvvy, Dads heard about you and he phoned Miss Crowley, and then you came to us for those week-ends, remember?'

'Yes, but how did he hear about me, Mm? How?' I persisted.

'Oh, it was through his office. D'you remember you didn't wash the bath out, and after you went back the second time, Gordon had a bath and he jumped out and said his ar– ... um ... bottom had been sand-papered – you'd forgotten to rinse the Vim off. We laughed, bless you. As Dads and me said, you'd tried!'

I was glad that I was sitting on the floor cleaning the sticky shelves so that she didn't see my face red with embarrassment. I felt hurt and ashamed. What else had they laughed at about me? She still hadn't answered my question as to how they had heard about me and after a long silence I began again.

'What office does, eh . . . Dads work at? Where is it?'

'Never you mind, young lady. I'm not going to answer any more of your questions and you're not to ask, understand?'

6

The following day was Saturday, and it was my first encounter with Arthur Oakes since the last brutal incident. From my room I could hear him talking to his wife in the garden. The persistent opening and closing of the front door told me that Gordon was doing his usual Saturday morning overhaul of his bubble-car. I walked into the dining-room and a shock ran through my body as I found myself alone with Mr Oakes. He was reading the newspaper. Through the french windows I could see Mrs Oakes at the bottom of the garden.

'’Ello, luv. Feeling better, are you?'

Gordon was right: his father did look like Christie in his steel-rimmed glasses. I didn't answer him, but picked up the pen and pad that lay on the sideboard and went to the dining-table to make out the weekend shopping list. He came over from the french windows, where he'd been holding the paper up to the light – perhaps his 'Christie' glasses weren't as strong as the pair he'd broken. I'd heard from Mrs Oakes that the night he'd had the 'bad' fish cakes, he'd been so sick he'd lost his specs down the toilet bowl, and had broken the side-piece fishing them out. I was amazed that he could have thought up a story like that.

'Feelin' better?' he repeated, sitting down opposite me.

'Yes, thanks.' I didn't look up, and continued to write items in columns headed Grocer, Greengrocer, Chemist and Hardware. My hands were trembling, so I put down the pen and sat on them lest he should notice. I gazed intently at the list and saw his hand reach out. I withdrew my body swiftly, thrusting it backwards in the chair, but he only reached into the fruit bowl and retrieved an orange. He began to throw the orange gently from one hand to the other. Keeping my eyes on the orange, like a spectator at Wimbledon, I saw him eventually put the fruit down and walk across to the sideboard. From the drawer he took a cork-backed place-mat and a strange implement, which looked like a cross between a very peculiar corkscrew and one of Mrs Oakes's crochet hooks. He returned to his seat at the table and placed the orange on top of the place-mat.

'Watch this, luvvy.' With the top of the strange instrument he began to graze the sides of the orange until the peel fell away in sections like an open water-lily. Turning the instrument upside down, he scored the segments of fruit, which fell at each stroke until all the orange petals lay in full bloom.

'Go on, sweetheart.' He pointed to the segmented orange pieces with the hooked end of the instrument. 'Look, not a drop o' juice spilled. Mums and me bought it at the Ideal Home Exhibition at Earls Court when we went up to London. We go up every year. We'll take you.'

Not a drop of blood spilled, just scored flesh. Pith in white curved strips like my flesh. Orange flesh flecked with white and red, red speckled as my blood had been.

*

'Go on, luvvy, full of vitamin C.'

'No!' I felt a surge of anger like the one last Christmas that had made me tell Joan, our Child Care Officer, in front of our father, that the boys and Anna and I hadn't anything for Christmas: no tree, no decorations, no presents. The boys had dreaded the reprisals my outburst would surely bring, but instead it had brought about all the things we'd asked for and the biggest tree we'd ever had. Then it had been 'we'; now it was 'me' and the grief of being parted from them lay heavily on my chest, the ache once more rising to my throat. My first Christmas without them; what would I do?

'When's Miss Crowley coming?'

'I don't know. Why?'

'Because I want to see her.' He began pushing his glasses up and down his nose with his index finger at a furious pace. My next words came tumbling out. 'If you don't know when she's coming, when's Mr Knightley coming then?' This time I looked directly at him and the familiar beat of fear at the base of my spine began its painful throb.

His face had turned very pale and I saw fear in a man for the first time. The magical orange peeler in his hand was combing back at the sparse grey hair, disarraying the strands that had been carefully placed to conceal the bald pate. He jumped as the peeler struck the lenses of his glasses, and dropped the tool on the dining-table as if it had burned him.

I looked down at my shopping list with unseeing eyes, and heard his chair scrape back. A surreptitious glance showed me a stranger with 'naked' eyes polishing his glasses. His chair had been pulled closer to the table rather than scraped back as I had thought. Under the heading 'Grocer' my trembling hand began to write, '½lb Typhoo, 2lb gran. sugar, tin Nescafé, Ovaltine, ½lb Stork . . .' I heard Mr Oakes clear his throat gently. He tapped the table with the Ideal Home peeler.

'Look, sweetheart, I know what I did wasn't very nice, or you didn't think it was, but, eh, you know I wouldn't harm a hair of your head. You know that, don't you? Eh? Eh? See, let me explain. It's like, see, when you love somethin' so much, eh . . . you want to hug it so tight sometimes you hurt it. Can you understand that? I bet sometimes you've hugged little Anna so tight that she was nearly squashed to death. I bet I'm right, eh?'

At the mention of Anna's name tears welled in my eyes and spilled on to my cheeks. It was true that when she'd been in her pink siren suit, smelling of Johnson's Baby Powder, and had looked at me or said something clever, I'd squeezed her so hard she'd wriggled out of my grasp and slid to the floor. It was also true of Prowler; the last time I'd held him that hard was when my father said he was to be destroyed. I'd made him yelp as I squashed his ribs and kissed the top of his head. This was different, though. I knew it and so did Mr Oakes.

'Course, we can't stop you if you want to go. I'll phone Miss Crowley Monday morning. But I'll tell you this, it'll break Mums's heart and mine, even Gordon's.' This last reference made me want to protest, but I said nothing, I just sat rubbing the tears angrily from my face with the heel of my hand. 'Of course you could go to much worse than us, my *gurl*, much worse. Some of the people you hear about today, and the Homes – I've heard some things in my job, I can tell you!'

'What is your job?' I inquired, my voice almost a whisper.

'I'm with the Government. That's how I knew about you, luvvy. Us people in Government, we hear about children like you, see?'

My whole body stiffened; the painful throbbing began in the base of my spine. He knew about me, knew, as my father had said, that I'd murdered Mummy. My mind was racing. I could imagine him discussing my case with Harold Macmillan, the Prime Minister: 'We'll take her on, sir. We've got a lovely room for her at home, sir. My wife always wanted a daughter, sir.' What had he said? 'You could go to worse, much worse . . . I'll phone Miss Crowley on Monday morning . . . it'll break Mums's heart . . .'

'Artie! Artie! You can come and sort this damn compost out now, and I don't mean maybe! Have you finished that shopping list yet, young lady? It looks like it's only me and Gordon's familiar with work on a Saturday around here. He's fixed his wheel so's he can pick up my knitting machine this afternoon, but you couldn't be bothered to get the Hillman out last night when Izzie had a flat tyre!' Mrs Oakes stood at the french windows glowering at her husband. She wore her black wellington boots, an old tweed gardening skirt and an even more ancient jacket, yellow gardening gloves and a red woollen scarf, which had slipped down over her ears to reveal silver curlers glinting in the thin wintry sunshine.

Her eyes turned to me. That list should have been finished and the coffee done by now!' She glanced and poked at an imaginary watch on her wrist.

I picked up the shopping list and quickly rose to my

feet. Mr Oakes got up from the table at the same time, taking his place-mat, stripped orange and the peeler with him. We squeezed through the narrow kitchen door at the same time. Mrs Oakes had taken off her boots and was standing in a pair of thick woollen socks, still glaring at us both and puffing white air into the warm kitchen to ensure that we knew just how cold she was. I reached for the milk saucepan and proceeded to make the coffee. My eyes began to prick with unwanted tears again.

'Not more water works from you? Bloody 'ell, all I said was . . .'

I shook my head and said I still didn't feel very well. She said she didn't either but no one seemed to worry about her!

Time healed. Time, an invisible bandage that could be wrapped around an invisible pain but couldn't mend what had been taken away for ever, that was Mums's panacea for me. Her husband had just told me that he 'wouldn't hurt a hair on my head'. Our biology teacher had told us that hair was dead matter, so how could he hurt it? It didn't hurt to have your hair cut, only to have it pulled out. He wouldn't hurt a hair on my head, but he would hurt my body. I stirred the coffee furiously and set the four mugs on a tray with the Saturday ginger biscuits.

'Aah! There's a good girl. Did you put essence of rennet down on the list and the mincemeat and the tin of shortcake? Lummy, Christmas is nearly on top of us!'

I muttered my apologies for the omissions and ran into the kitchen to write the list as fast as I could, grateful for the chance to catch up and to be alone. Mrs

63

Oakes came out to the kitchen just as I was writing 'bundles of wood' under Hardware.

'Got my Friars Ball–sum? Bun–yun pads?'

'No, sorry, you didn't . . .'

'I did! When you were doin' the cupboards out, I said don't let me forget – still they're only for me.' She sniffed in disgust.

Mr Oakes appeared with the tray of coffee mugs. 'Gordon's not finished his yet, and you've not started yours. Now then, *gurl*, when you've had yours, you can wash them up while Mums has a good warm through. She's perished!'

I quickly drank some of the once pleasurable liquid and emptied the rest down the sink as soon as they had left the kitchen. Gordon came in just as I was drying the last mug and placed his on the wooden draining-board with a grunt that I now knew to be his thanks. From the dining-room came the sound of Mrs Oakes taking out her curlers and dropping them one by one into a tin with a clink, punctuated only by 'bugger!' when the occasional curler refused to release itself with ease from bondage in the white, wiry hair.

That Saturday was the day Mr Oakes gave me a new name. He was to call me *gurl* for the rest of my stay with the Oakes family.

7

November 5th brought back so many memories. I wondered if the boys were having a bonfire. I saw one or two guys while I was doing my paper round, and occasionally rockets or bangers could be heard in these new skies. Mrs Oakes had told me in no uncertain terms that they didn't have 'penny for the guying' where we lived because, firstly, it was 'begging' and, secondly, we lived in a 'lete' place. I wondered if that meant it was against the law here, and decided to look up 'lete' in the dictionary. I tried 'lete', 'leat', and finally 'leet', but couldn't find it. I'd have to ask Pauline.

It was on that Guy Fawkes night that Gordon sprang a big surprise. I'd spent two nights doing an evening paper round because one of the boys was ill. I'd seen some very small bonfires in gardens, and rockets and bangers seemed to be going off nearly as regularly as they did in London. Pauline hadn't known what 'lete' meant, but then said she wasn't very 'up' on big words. She did tell me, however, that they had bonfires and guys and fireworks where she lived.

The familiar sulphurous smell of spent fireworks brought back the pain of being without Mummy, my grandmother and the boys. Last year Anna had liked the Roman candles, the Catherine wheels and the fire, but she'd been frightened of the bangers, so I'd had to

take her in. This was the night of ginger beer and potatoes in their jackets, often only half cooked, with blobs
of margarine to soften the hardened flesh, the night
when grown-ups would place chestnuts on the fringe of
the fire on big shovels, then retrieve them from the
embers tasting deliciously of nutty charcoal.

Taylor's, the newsagent, had sold out of fireworks,
but Mr Taylor had some sparklers left and let me buy a
box of matches because he said he could trust me. When
I finished my round, I walked to the entrance of an
alleyway separating the tall garden walls and lit each
one, tears coursing down my cheeks until the last spark
had faded and the red ember turned black on the steel
stick. The 'Poppy Day' words came back to me – 'We
will remember them.' Like them, the sparklers had
briefly lit my life and had now left me in darkness.

'You're late and you're freezing, ducks. Go on in or
you'll catch your death,' Mrs Oakes chided.

I would have liked to counter that 'death had caught
me' as I lived this night of memories, but she looked full
of concern and rubbed my cold face gently with her
knuckles.

'I'll just go and wash.' I put my paper bag under the
telephone table in the hall and ran upstairs.

'I'll make you a nice hot drink, luvvy,' she called up
after me.

I washed my hands and face in case she should see
that the 'waterworks' had been turned on. From the
bathroom I could hear someone in the garden. Mrs
Oakes was waiting for me with a cup of hot tea when I
walked into the kitchen. The smell of rabbit casserole
seasoned with bay leaves filled the room, and I suddenly
felt very sick. I'd only recently been introduced to rabbit

66

and I couldn't bear to think of eating such beautiful creatures. I had visions of Walt Disney's Thumper in the big glazed pot. Mrs Oakes had said how much I'd liked it before I knew what it was and I shouldn't be fussy, but tonight I couldn't eat rabbit whatever she said.

In the dining-room Mr Oakes was reading the newspaper that I brought back every morning.

'Hello.' He looked up briefly.

'It's cold.' I held my palms out to the fire.

'Umm . . . How long will the meal be, Kath?'

'Ready now, come on out to the kitchen both of you, quickly!'

I looked at him but he averted his eyes. His glasses had been mended and he looked much kinder in his real ones. I followed him out of the room. A shaft of freezing air assaulted us from the open kitchen door.

'C'mon, you two!' Mrs Oakes sounded excited.

'Close the door, *gurl*. We've had to put Blimp in the lounge. Dining and kitchen. C'mon.'

Silently I obeyed and closed both doors. The back door was wide open, however, and when I stepped outside I saw Gordon standing over a bonfire that had just started to take hold. Orange, yellow and blue flames were licking their way up through various bits of wooden crates and what looked like a broken-up chest of drawers and two old wooden chairs. Underneath, a carpet of crimson embers had begun to unfold. Other jigsaw pieces of wood and papers crackled and lit the garden I had once loved and maybe would again, if only once a year.

Mrs Oakes propelled me gently down the garden path towards the fire. On the stone garden wall there sat a huge box of Benwell's fireworks. For the next twenty minutes or so we stood watching as Gordon lit rockets from empty milk bottles, just as we used to. Catherine wheels spun their furious riot of colours on the wooden washing-line post. There were Roman candles, and silver and golden rain poured out in fountains. A purple spray caused Mrs Oakes to break into song – 'When the Deep Purple Falls over Sleepy Garden Walls' – and when Gordon put a huge Catherine wheel on to the wooden post, she shouted, 'Gor–don, if that line goes up, you pay for it, and I don't mean maybe!'

Jumping Jacks frightened Mrs Oakes, and Mr Oakes was furious when Gordon lit two at once, sending her screaming towards the house yelling 'Artie! Artie! Those jackers are after me!'

'That's enough, son,' his father admonished, and I was afraid he might see me laughing.

'You haven't got any of them bangers, Gordon? 'Cos if you have . . .' Mrs Oakes was really enjoying all this, and looked pretty in the glow of the fire, her cheeks flushed.

'No, Ma! I don't like them myself, you know that!' Gordon spoke for the first time. 'C'mon, this is the last one and it's the best.'

I'd never seen a firework as big as this. It was a huge pyramid shape and its colours went from red to orange to gold, green, silver and blue. One last burst brought forth a scattering of all the colours. A strange quiet and sense of anti-climax descended on us as we made our way back towards the kitchen door.

'Wasn't that luverly, eh? He's a naughty boy with those jackers, though. He knows my nerves get bad,' Mrs Oakes giggled at her son's pranks.

I had to agree it was a lovely surprise, and asked if Gordon did that every year.

'Oh no! Not for years and years, ducks!'

'Dampen that down now, son. We don't want the garage alight,' Mr Oakes called out. He was first in the single file as we approached the kitchen door, his wife next and I was last. As he opened the kitchen door there was an enormous explosion. Mrs Oakes screamed and clutched at somewhere on her right below her ribcage, where her 'heart failure' was coming on. Mr Oakes swore loudly as he tried to heave his wife into the kitchen. Once inside she seemed to recover from her failing heart and was breathlessly telling 'Artie' to see if her boy was all right. I knew 'her boy' was all right, and I knew what he'd done.

Gordon sauntered up the garden path, having thrown a bucket of water over the fire to dowse it, and swaggered into the kitchen to refill the bucket.

'Oh, Gordon, luvvy, are you all right? Put the kettle on, ducks. No, I'll have a sherry, settle my nerves. They've gone they really have, it was like the Blitz all over again!'

'Er ... there must have been some bangers in the bottom of the box when I threw it on. I didn't know, I swear, honestly!' Gordon's voice was raised above the rush of water from the tap into the galvanized metal bucket.

'Gordon! When that fire is out, you can get in here and clean yourself up. You knew there were bangers in that box, so don't lie to me, my boy!' His mother was gulping at some amber liquid Mr Oakes had put in a tumbler for her.

'You could have given your mother a heart attack, son,' his father interjected.

'You get up to that bathroom and wash, Gor–don, and I don't mean maybe!'

When he returned for the last bucket, Gordon's face was smudged with black, even his grey hair had black streaks in it, and he smelled deliciously of a hundred bonfires and spent fireworks. For the first time ever he looked at me and gave a broad grin, even teeth showing brilliant white against his blackened face. He went upstairs and soon we heard the sound of running bathwater.

Mrs Oakes, now on her second tumbler of sherry, went into the hall. Steadying herself on the newel post, she shrieked up the stairs, 'Gor–don! Now you've let the casserole burn too!'

The bathwater stopped its churning, the taps seeming to groan at this untimely cessation. 'What?'

Mrs Oakes repeated her accusation.

'You shouldn't have put it on the bonfire, Ma. I told you it'd be better in the oven!'

'It was in the ... you cheeky young bugger! Out of my way!'

I dodged Gordon's mother as she wove dangerously across the kitchen with the blackened earthenware dish. The top was glued to the rim.

'You're all bloody well eating it, like it or not!' she shouted.

We did, and we did not!

It had been a strange bonfire night. Gordon had smiled at me, that was something. Perhaps he'd be nice to me now – perhaps.

8

Gordon's antics on that Guy Fawkes night did not bring about the change that I'd hoped for. He reverted to his usual surly self and I began to think that I had imagined the events of November 5th. But if I had imagined Gordon's smile, the loss of Mr Oakes's was real. These days he would usually address me from behind a newspaper. The word 'gurl' was used as if it were my name, supplanting the endearments 'sweetheart' and 'luvvy' of the past. I had come to accept these changes, and with Mrs Oakes's men at such a remove, I tried to draw closer to her. She seemed oblivious to any atmosphere, partly, I supposed, because of her knitting machine, which she had failed to master so far – a surprise to me, – and partly because the preparations for Christmas were under way at a frenetic pace.

Christmas card lists were a task Mrs Oakes gave to me, and invitations were sent out (as was customary I was to learn) to Auntie Ada and her daughter, Rose. These invitations had been duly accepted (which was also customary).

The lounge which I'd never seen used since my arrival, was opened. This room housed the radiogram, so it must have been used on those evenings when strains of John Hanson, Howard Keel and Nat King Cole could be heard vying with Mrs Oakes's renderings from *The*

Desert Song, *Carousel*, *Kismet* and *Oklahoma*. The first
time I'd heard her singing *Oklahoma* I thought someone
was being violently sick as the strange 'Oke – Oke –
Oke – lah – homa, where the wind comes sweeping
down the pah – lain' was belted out with gusto while I
tried to sleep. These performances became, in a strange
way, comforting once I'd grown used to her warblings.

Miss Crowley came to see me at the beginning of
December. To be fair to Mr Oakes, he wasn't at all
smarmy, unlike my father, who would have switched on
the charm for her and would surely have melted even
this cold, rather austere person with his warm Celtic
charisma. Mr Oakes, however, was as cool and clipped
with her as he was with me. She didn't seem to notice or
mind, but perhaps because he was in the Government
he could act this way with her. Mrs Oakes brought in
the usual tray of tea and biscuits and discussed the
difficulty she was having with the knitting machine.
This seemed to intrigue Miss Crowley, who eventually
announced it had to be a fault with the machine and
not the operator. Mrs Oakes became very coy and told
the Child Care Officer that she was going to pack it
away in the cupboard under the stairs and have another
go after Christmas. In the meantime, she said, I had lots
of hand-knitted garments, which was true.

'It's so luverly having a child in the house at Christmas. We're having a tree and decorations this year,
aren't we, dear? Well, if you'll excuse us, Miss Crowley,
I know you'll want to see, eh, Caroline on her own.' Mr
and Mrs Oakes left the room as they usually did.

'Well, how are we, my deah?'

'Fine, thank you. Have you heard anything about
Anna and the boys?'

'Well, my deah, all settling into their new lives and very happy I believe. How was your school report, umm?'

'We haven't broken up yet.'

'No, of course, how silly of me!'

'Can . . . have you seen any of them?'

'Your family? No, my deah, but this is your new family now and . . .'

'Can I send them Christmas presents? You see, I've got my paper round and I've seen –'

'Oh, Caroline, they'll have lots and lots of presents, just as you will, I'm sure. Perhaps we could see about you sending a Christmas card?'

'Yes, I'll do that, if you give me their addresses.'

'Look, deah, send them to me at my office, and I'll pass them on to someone who –'

'You tell me where they are! You do know, you bloody old liar, you do, so tell me!' An ugly sob escaped from my throat and a heavy silence hung in the air.

Miss Crowley's voice was gentle for the first time since I'd known her, and she put out a hand that had the same texture as a russet apple. 'Caroline, I don't know where they are, really. I can only send your Christmas cards on to the big office in London. I'm sure that they will pass them on. Now drink your tea, my deah.' The rough-skinned hand slid from mine.

'I've embroidered a tablecloth for Granny. Can you send that to the London people's office too?' I asked hopefully.

'Yes. May I see it?'

Tears were drying on my face, making it feel taut, and my nose was running. Miss Crowley handed me a folded handkerchief; it was a man's, like those I'd bought for Gordon and Mr Oakes for Christmas.

'I'll go and get it,' I sniffed, making for the door. On the stairs I collided with Gordon.

'You need bloody L plates,' he snapped at me.

Ignoring him, I took the tablecloth from the shelf behind the frills on the dressing-table. It was in a paper bag, grubby in places where I'd worked chain and satin stitches into the stiff material. I'd started it in school and Mrs Oakes had helped me finish it. I'd bought Christmas cards at Taylor's, and now selected the one I'd intended for Pauline and wrote: 'Granny, I miss you and everyone. Please tell me where everyone is. Can I come and live with you please ask THEM. Lots of love and kisses, Caroline. xxxxxxxxxx' I put my address on the card in huge capital letters in case Granny's eyes were getting worse. I picked out the cards I'd bought for Auntie Ada and Rose and wrote one to the boys and one to Anna. I took the package wrapped in holly-printed paper that contained the hankies meant for Gordon and slipped it between the folds of the table-cloth, gathered up the cards and ran back down the stairs.

'Well it's bound to be, it is her first –' Mrs Oakes broke off in mid-sentence as I came back into the room with the bag and cards.

'So lovely for all of you, such exciting plans for Christmas and I'd love to see your face on Christmas morning, Caroline, I really would, your mother here was just telling me . . .'

I stood waiting, the package held tightly to me, as Mrs Oakes left the room.

'Let me see. Mrs Oakes says you've a natural talent for needlework and cookery. Oh, how pretty! Your grandmother will be delighted and proud, I shouldn't wonder!'

'These are the cards, and this is for you.' I handed her the wrapped handkerchiefs and retrieved the table-cloth, which she had draped over her wrist, folded it and replaced it in its bag. 'I haven't got any wrapping paper, but Granny won't mind. I'll put the cards in here so that they won't get lost.' I snatched the cards she was holding, and she stood there obviously wondering if I was going to retrieve the holly-papered package too. 'That is for you, Miss Crowley, er ... and a Happy Christmas.'

'Oh, Caroline, what a thoughtful child. That really is very sweet of you. Thank you very much, you really are very sweet to do this,' she repeated.

Oh no I'm not, Miss Crowley. I don't think about you at all until something dreadful happens and then I know I wouldn't be able to tell you even if I did see you. I'm not sweet either, Miss Crowley, I'm not sweet at all. I hate you Miss Crowley!

'Well, my deah, I must be going. I have a little some-thing here for you too, not to be opened until Christmas Day, mind! Mr and Mrs Oakes have lots of wonderful surprises for you, you know,' her voice broke into a confidential whisper, 'though I shouldn't be saying.'

Yes, Miss Crowley, Mr Oakes has already given me one or two surprises, as you call them, Miss Crowley.

I was holding the card and the oblong package wrapped in Santa Claus paper she had extended to me, which I had received with effusive thanks. I would have kissed her roughened hand if I thought that Granny was

75

going to get that card, the card that was an SOS from me.

'Thank you for the present. I'm sorry I swore at you. I didn't mean it, Miss Crowley,' I whispered.

'Shush, it's forgotten, my deah. You're very lucky to be here with such an understanding and loving family.'

'Yes, I know,' I lied once again. 'You could go to worse than us, my *gurl* ...' Mr Oakes's words came back, hauntingly, tauntingly. They knew. My father had told them I'd murdered Mummy and this was where you went, but if you didn't behave, they'd put you in worse places, where there'd be Mr Oakeses and Gordons and Miss Crowleys and no Mrs Oakes at all.

It was time for the Oakeses to say their goodbyes. I flinched as I stood at the front door and heard Miss Crowley say she'd see me next year. Next year? A whole year?

'Not for another year?' I asked her incredulously, suddenly afraid I wouldn't see her for twelve months. Much as I disliked her, she was my link with the London people.

'Oh deah, no! I should have said the New Year, January, of course!' She turned and laughed, and Mr and Mrs Oakes laughed too.

'Oh yes, well, happy New Year,' I called over my shoulder, and went into the dining-room to lay the table for dinner. I heard them talking in low tones on the doorstep. Their voices became louder as they wished one another a happy Christmas and New Year. As I heard the door shut, I went to run upstairs to my room and ran straight into Mr Oakes.

'Aah!' I exclaimed.

'Where you goin' then, *gurl*? Upstairs to your bed-room, eh, eh?'

Miserably I nodded.

'Oh no you don't! You can take that tray into the kitchen. You don't lay the table around a used tea tray, for God's sake. What's the matter with you? Mums isn't gonna wait on you either, so pull your socks up and go and see if you can help her in the kitchen.' Once again he was pushing his glasses up and down the bridge of his nose.

Mrs Oakes was pricking sausages, stabbing at them with a fork as if they were vermin, to be destroyed at all costs. I washed and dried the tea things as quickly and quietly as possible.

'Sanatogen!' she exclaimed in a loud voice.

I didn't know if this was a swear-word, or understand what it was the prelude to.

'Sanatogen Tonic Wine for my nerves, and I'm gonna get drunk on it, and I don't mean maybe!' she continued and began to sing 'What'll I Do When You Are Far Away?', which, I'd noticed, she always sang when she was in a bad mood. She had barely begun when she interrupted her sad song to screech 'Gor–don!' as her eyes rested on an oily piece of metal on the draining-board that I'd carefully avoided while I washed up.

I made a swift exit from the kitchen and was about to ascend the stairs when Gordon came in through the front door, cold air rushing in with him. His hands were covered in oil and he was wiping them on an equally oily rag. He arched his eyebrows inquiringly at me and then comprehension flickered in his eyes. 'Oh shit!' he said softly, heading towards the kitchen and his mother's wrath.

Dinner that night was a tense affair. Mr Oakes had turned *The Archers* up to nearly full volume and Walter Gabriel's rasping, gravelly voice was almost pleasurable to hear.

Later I lay in bed, my thoughts scattered like the bits and pieces of coloured glass in the kaleidoscope Mummy had bought me one Christmas, except there were no pretty patterns in the fragmented pieces of my life now. I wondered why Mrs Oakes always sang that song when she was sad and her 'rhythm' song when she was happy. I couldn't imagine how she could like her husband or Gordon, not really. My thoughts turned from her to whether Granny would get the tablecloth and my SOS. The boys and Anna, would they be given my cards? Why was everyone in such a bad mood? Had that Crowley woman said that I'd called her a bloody liar? Had she told them about Mummy and – no, go, go, leave me, please, memory. Don't let Mummy's death . . . the orange candle flared, its now familiar flame licked and I recoiled as I thought of her and my father's accusation. My heart burned briefly and the flame became an empty smoke ring.

Footsteps on the stairs and outside my room. It was strange, but I no longer feared that door opening, and when it did and he was standing there, I still felt that what he had done he would never do again. I could even understand the situation I was now in with him. Still, I was surprised to hear my voice shout 'No!' He was fully dressed. I didn't expect him to be anything else, no stranger with 'naked' eyes and maroon-striped pyjamas, breathing heavily. Just him in grey trousers and a navy-blue sweater, glasses screening eyes I no longer wanted to see.

He strode across the bedroom to my dressing-table and clicked off the bakelite button on the lamp, throwing the bedroom into darkness.

'I want that out by nine every night now, *gurl*. You're wasting my electricity and I pay for it, understand? Nine o'clock, eh, eh?'

'Yes, I heard you, I bloody heard you. Go away, go away.'

'Don't you dare speak to . . .' He didn't finish the sentence, just strode out of the room, leaving me in a new kind of darkness.

I didn't cry at first but lay there wondering why every time I had rebelled and shouted at a grown-up – at Joan last Christmas about our lack of presents, at Mr Oakes that Saturday in the dining-room, and now, twice in one day, I'd even sworn at Miss Crowley and him – I had received no real punishment. I might receive some tomorrow, though. Defiantly, I switched the lamp back on, took out my kitten box and held the pink scarf to my face. I took the black shiny curl from its envelope and, stroking it gently, wound it round and round in the palm of my hand. *I still have part of her with me, Mr Oakes, and tonight I can smell and touch her. She was my armour, my mother, and no one can ever take that away from me, Mr Oakes, not even you.*

9

Christmas Cards arrived every day for the Oakeses,
which rather confused me, as we'd had so few Christmas
cards sent to us at home although Mummy and Granny
had had lots more friends than this family. Every day I
watched and waited for a reply from my grandmother,
but none came.

Pauline's parents had said we could have a Christmas
tree cheap from their stall in the market, and I ran
home fit to burst to impart this good news to Mrs
Oakes. I was bewildered when she refused their kindness. The Oakeses would order one from their greengrocer, of whom they'd been 'asteemed' customers since
before the war, thank you all the same, Mrs Oakes had
informed me, pulling herself up to her full height, her
mouth pursed. I had to lie to Pauline that the Oakeses
were ever so grateful, but they'd already bought one.

Gordon and his father brought the Christmas tree
home and put it in the lounge. Gordon and his mother
let me help to trim the tree. Some of the decorations
were tarnished, but Gordon had taken his mother to
Woolworth's and they'd bought tinsel and some new
coloured glass balls. A glittery silver star was attached
to the very top of the tree with a pipe-cleaner. I was
glad it wasn't a fairy doll, which would have been too
much of a reminder of Anna, who was still clutching

the Christmas fairy from our tree when she was taken from me.

Gordon and Mr Oakes decorated the lounge with garlands with the same precision they'd shown in changing the curtains. Holly did indeed 'deck the halls', and the perfume of the fresh pine-needles seemed to reach through my nostrils down to the back of my throat, and settle in a heavy mass of pain on my chest. I was to realize through the years that my most acute memories of grief were provoked by scent and music.

I had finished my Christmas shopping. I'd replaced the handkerchiefs I'd bought for Gordon and given to Miss Crowley, or the 'Old Crow' as Pauline had christened her, and I'd bought Pauline a pair of shocking-pink and green luminous socks. Acting for me, Pauline's sister, Deirdre, had bought a bottle of Sanatogen Tonic Wine for Mrs Oakes, which had cost more than I'd expected. I knew they wouldn't sell me wine in the off-licence, but Deirdre said she'd bought it in the chemist, which surprised me a bit. She thought it a funny sort of present, so I decided it probably wasn't enough and bought a small box of chocolates as well.

Auntie Ada and cousin Rose were due to arrive on 23 December, and Mrs Oakes advised that twenty Gold-Flake cigarettes would please Auntie Ada, and that Rose would want some bath salts. I'd made these purchases and had wrapped all my presents except the Sanatogen wine, which was proving difficult; I had to buy a whole sheet of wrapping paper before I succeeded.

A mattress had been brought down from the attic by Mr Oakes and Gordon and had been toasting by the fire for the past three days. Mrs Oakes explained to me that I would have to sleep in the lounge over Christmas, as Auntie Ada and Rose had had my room every Christmas and summer holiday since 'the old king died', as she put it.

Now the bedroom was no longer mine, and I gazed around it. The chest of drawers had been removed from the recess and seemed to have welded itself to the wardrobe. My bed had a twin, with twin eiderdown, sheets and pillowslips, which stood in the recess. I had to empty my chest of drawers for Auntie Ada and Rose and put my belongings in the airing cupboard in the bathroom. Mrs Oakes gave me a box to put my underwear and socks in, and another for my jumpers. My coat, jacket and three winter dresses and skirts had been pushed flush against the interior of the wardrobe, and there were about eight empty coat-hangers for Auntie Ada and Rose. My school uniform was hanging in Mr and Mrs Oakes's wardrobe.

'OK, ducks?' Mrs Oakes asked as she helped me fold my jumpers and blouses neatly in the larger box. 'There now, I'll leave you to put your undies and bits and bobs in the other box. Come here. Look, I've put your pillow and sheets and blankets on the top there. Can you reach? If you fold 'em up each morning and put 'em back, it'll only take us a couple of minutes to straighten the lounge out. To be honest, I enjoy sleeping down there, and I have many a time when Dads and me have had words! "Everything's in rhythm with my heart, the moonlight, the June night . . .",' she burst into song and left me to put my underwear, pyjamas and nightdress in the smaller box.

I placed my kitten box at the very bottom and folded everything else on top. I put my deodorant, talc and an old lipstick and tiny, round blue box of rouge that

Pauline's sister had given me in my school satchel, which I pushed under the sofa in the lounge. I put my shoes behind the two boxes and went downstairs. Everything was still in rhythm with Mrs Oakes's heart apparently and she was checking the jars of pickled onions she'd shown me how to make back in September, along with her red cabbage, mixed pickles and chutneys.

On the morning of the twenty-third the butcher arrived with a huge leg of pork and an enormous turkey. I'd seen turkeys before, but only hanging up in the butchers' shops; I'd never tasted one.

That morning's paper round had been really heavy and my shoulders ached. The other paper boys and the only other girl advised me to knock on the doors and wish everyone a Merry Christmas and people would give me my Christmas-box. I didn't want to, nor, as it happened, did I need to. People came out and gave me a shilling, a florin or a half-crown. One person, a doctor, gave me five shillings on Christmas Eve.

Mr Oakes had gone to meet the London train bearing Auntie Ada and Rose at one o'clock.

They arrived just as I returned from getting Mrs Oakes some shopping. It was like walking into a classroom where the teacher hasn't yet appeared: everyone seemed to be talking at once!

Auntie Ada was extremely fat and had white hair, the front of which swept back in a trail of dark orange. Her dark brown laughing eyes disappeared among the folds of fat, and the rest of her face seemed to lift every time she broke into raucous laughter. White face powder failed to cover the broad red nose while deep crimson lipstick guarded the dentures, which would collapse down, only to be drawn upwards with a clacking noise

83

in defiance of the laws of gravity. Two orangey-brown tram-lines ran from her nostrils to join the bows of crimson lips. This strange jaundiced effect fascinated me until I heard Gordon say she should distribute her smoke more evenly to give herself an overall suntan and henna her hair too. I still didn't understand, so Mrs Oakes explained it was the nicotine from the cigarettes Auntie Ada chain-smoked that caused her strange colouring.

Auntie Ada wore a baby-pink twin set – her breasts seemed to have found their place of rest at the base of her ribcage – and a brown pleated skirt of an enormous expanse, the pleats billowing out like a huge concertina. Lisle stockings encompassed broad tree-trunk legs, and short brown suede boots with a zipper at the front covered disproportionately small feet.

''Ere she is then, luv 'er.' Auntie Ada enveloped me in a bear-hug. Auntie Ada smelled. Auntie Ada smelled of tobacco, gravy and wet knickers, but I was reluctant to break from her embrace. 'Lets 'ave a look at 'er, then!' Holding me at arm's length, she smiled, bringing her eyes up and teeth down. 'Ooh, she's grown! Put on weight an' all. Feelin' better, are ya, darlin'?'

'Yes, thank you, Auntie.'

'Ooh, she's bleedin' luvly, she is an' all.' Once again my head was enveloped in folds of soft flesh until I had to turn my head to one side to breathe. Releasing me, she cupped my face in her surprisingly small hands with their tawny fingers. Lifting my head, Auntie Ada kissed me full on the mouth. Her chins and upper lip sported autumnal bronze hairs.

'She's gonna be a little beauty, well she is now, ain't she, Kaff?'

Mrs Oakes seemed to accede to this compliment, but I couldn't tell what her expression was, as my eyes were set upon the dead pine needles that sprouted from Auntie Ada's nostrils. She still held both of my cheeks in her gentle, but vice-like grip. No matter; I loved Auntie Ada. I had when I'd first met her and I'd forgotten how I'd warmed to her then, although she hadn't been as demonstrative as she was now. Her daughter, Rose, was another matter.

Having at last released me, Auntie Ada still kept a covetous arm around my shoulders while with her free arm she managed to extract a cigarette from a packet on the dining-table, light it and inhale so deeply I could almost feel the black bellow of lung absorb the blue smoke.

Rose had her arms encircled firmly around Mr and Mrs Oakes's shoulders. Their cheeks were pressed so close to hers that you had the impression you were looking at a three-headed monster. Both her aunt and uncle were smiling indulgently at this unabashed demonstration of affection from their niece.

'Ooh, it's so luverly t' be back fer Christmas, Auntie and Unc,' she squealed.

'Coo, Rosie luv, put me down. You don't know where I've been,' her aunt protested.

Rosie relaxed her grasp on the Oakeses, and they both gave audible sighs of relief and laughingly said she'd make a great all-in wrestler. Suddenly Rosie's eyes widened as she looked at the baking tin that held the turkey.

'Blimey, Mum, look at the size o' that bird this year! Every year we says they can't get no bigger, but the buggers do!'

''Ere now, nark, it, my gel, wiv this little 'un around. Watch yer mawf an' yer bleedin' language!' Auntie Ada admonished.

Rosie put her tongue out at her mother and, glowering at me, strode across the kitchen to where the huge white and black-speckled corpse lay spread-eagled on the vast baking tray.

'Blimey, wot a porker!' Auntie Ada exclaimed as she joined her daughter to examine the exhibit. Rosie's crimon-painted index finger prodded the bird's plump white breast, and her mother's amber one joined it, as if they were both tuning a piano.

'No, Ada, it's not a porker, it's a turkey,' Mr Oakes quipped.

'Oh, go on wiv ya Artie, yer a caution.' Auntie Ada proceeded to dig her brother-in-law in the ribs, which caused more chaos in the confines of the narrow kitchen. 'Artie', I was learning, was ticklish.

'No more, Ada,' he protested as he recovered his breath. The shrieks this charade had elicited from Mr Oakes were almost girlish. He held his hands against his puny chest in defence and another primeval cry issued from his thin lips as Rosie embarked on further stabs at her uncle's chest.

'That's enough, you silly buggers. I'm trying to make a pot of tea here. Oi! I said, that's enough!' Mrs Oakes's voice caused the cacophony to cease. 'Take the girls' cases up to their room, Artie, and their coats.'

'No, no, don't take 'em up yet, Unc,' Rosie protested breathlessly. 'I've got me presents to put away an' I don't want no peekin'.' Rosie's heavy body pushed past me as she lumberered into the hall, only to reappear within seconds. 'We got the same room, ain't we, Auntie, Unc?'

'Yes, luvvy, same as always,' Mr Oakes, still breathless from the horseplay, affirmed.

'Oh, 'scuse. 'Ello again, luv.' Rosie, it seemed, had decided to recognize my existence. 'Where d'ya kip then, eh?'

'I'm sleeping in there while you're staying,' I replied, inclining my head towards the hallway and the lounge.

'Oh, ya sleep in our room normal like then, eh?'

I nodded. Even the room wasn't mine, not really – I'd borrowed it. I felt very near to tears and blinked hard. Auntie Ada put a huge arm around my shoulders.

'We kicked ya out of 'ouse an' 'ome darlin', 'ave we?'

'No, no, I don't mind, honestly,' I lied. Auntie Ada shook me gently, kissed the top of my head and released me.

'C'mon then, Rosie, let's git them bits upstairs, an' our Artie can bring our cases up.' The kitchen shook as they thundered up the stairs, and the brief silence that followed was broken by Rosie yelling 'All clear'. On cue Mr Oakes left the kitchen to carry their luggage up to what had been my room.

'She's a one, our Rosie, isn't she, ducks? Be a good girl and use the other teapot as well; they like their cuppas.'

I didn't answer, but took the plates of sandwiches and cake into the dining-room. The dining-table had been extended, and I'd set places for six. Mrs Oakes came in carrying a heavy tray of teapots, milk and hot-water jugs and a sugar basin, calling upstairs that tea was on the table and adding a harsh 'now! and I don't mean maybe' for Artie.

'Tuck in,' Mrs Oakes advised, and the room seemed to shudder as everyone assembled. I was unsure where I should sit until Mrs Oakes indicated the seat at the top

87

of the table, and I sat down with my back to the french windows. Auntie Ada and Rosie were in no such quandary and took the seats to my right. Mr and Mrs Oakes sat to my left, and the empty place opposite me was obviously Gordon's.

''Ere, where's Go-Go?' Rosie was sitting nearest to me, tearing a piece of ham from the middle of the sandwich with her amazing teeth. Each large yellow tooth seemed to overlay another at right angles. The front two looked almost as if they were clasped in an obscure handshake. Rosie seemed neither old nor young to me. Her skin was flawless and she had her mother's dark brown eyes, although they were much larger, with short, thick black lashes. Her eyebrows were black and dense and met at the bridge of her long, broad nose. Full lips and a heavy jaw gave her a rather masculine look, and her cheeks were as highly coloured as the crimson lipstick had been, smudges of which were now adorning discarded crusts of bread on her plate.

Her hair had a sickly sweetish odour. It was coarse, frizzy in places, tightly curled in a rather shapeless permanent wave, and its dark brown colour was embroidered with strands of silvery wire. It was, however, her hands that fascinated me. I surreptitiously glanced at Mr Oakes's, which were positively dainty by comparison, and felt a shudder of unwarranted fear go through me. Rosie's hands were the size of a very large man's and the crimson-painted fan-shaped nails evoked something of a Lewis Carroll nightmare in me.

'Well, where is 'e then?'

I jumped at the sound of Rosie's voice, imagining that the Duchess from Wonderland was addressing this little Alice.

88

'Doesn't finish till four o'clock,' Mrs Oakes was saying.

'Still got that queer little car, 'as 'e then?' Rosie, still chewing, took a noisy gulp of tea, as if to swallow the question.

'Coo, I'll say! Loves that little car, he does, doesn't he, Artie? I still wish he'd get somethin' a bit more ... well, solid I s'pose. Here, have a piece of vikki, Ada, Rosie?' Mrs Oakes pointed to the Victoria sandwich that I'd made.

'Ta,' Auntie Ada and Rosie said in unison, proffering their plates.

'Our little girl 'ere made this, didn't you, ducks, eh?' Mrs Oakes was beaming at me and I felt my cheeks go the colour of the crimson fingernails to my right.

'Well, I never did, Kaff. S'luvly an' light an' all. She's gonna make some bloke a good li'l wife someday, ain't ya, darlin'?' I looked up and smiled at Auntie Ada, who wasn't even looking my way. I quickly averted my eyes as I saw Rosie's crimson-tipped shovel take another slice of 'vikki'.

'She's quiet, ain't she, Kaff? Don't eat much neever, eh?' Auntie Ada was speaking to Mrs Oakes as if I wasn't there.

'Oh you're all right, ain't you, luvvy? I expect she's tired. She's up at the crack o' sparrer, as you'd say, Ada, to do her paper round and then there's all the excitement of Christmas an' all.'

I murmured that I was fine, and watched blue smoke spiralling over the table as Auntie Ada and Rosie lit their cigarettes.

'Shall I ...?' I began, and Mrs Oakes nodded her approval.

I was on my feet immediately, stacking the used tea plates and knives, and was nearly out of the dining-room door when the knives clattered to the floor.

'Don't be clever now, gurl. A few at a time. A couple of journeys won't hurt you. Now start again.'

Hurt and humiliated, I replaced the tea plates and knives on the table, wishing I could throw each one at him as I'd once seen someone do in a circus act at the pictures – only each knife would be on target and there would be no crowd to grasp at the near miss. The only gasp would be his, his last.

'Sorry,' I said softly.

I made four or five journeys back and forth. By my last trip a thick blue haze hung over the room.

'Shall I leave Gordon's?' I asked.

Mr Oakes placed a hand on my arm and I put the two teapots back on the table, thinking I was overloading again.

'Hey, hey, young lady! What is it that saves shoe leather and begins with "t" and ends with "y", eh?'

'I know, Artie, it's a blakey!' Auntie Ada exclaimed triumphantly.

'Nope.' Mr Oakes shook his head, his hand still on my arm. He was looking up at me, his other index finger pushing his glasses up and down, up and down, on his nose. A wry smile played on his lips. 'Begins with a "t", not a "b", Ada. Since when has blakey begun with "t"? Well?'

I knew he could feel my arm trembling. Although his touch was light, it was enough to stay me.

'Saves shoe levver, begins wiv a "t", ends wiv a "y."' Rosie was speaking very slowly, knitting her heavy eyebrows together so tightly that they formed a black moustache across her eyes. She was opening and closing her thick lips like a goldfish making blue rings in a pool, but these were smoke rings in the air. 'I know, Unc, I know.' She banged a huge hand upon the table, which at least made Mr Oakes remove his hand from my arm. 'It's "tootsy," Unc! It is, ain't it, Unc?'

'Nope! She'll tell you, won't you, gurl, eh?'

Everyone now looked expectantly towards me. My face burned and I shook my head. A strange perplexity seemed to permeate the very atmosphere and mingle with the blue blanket of smoke that hung in the room.

'Don't know?'

I shook my head.

'A tray, gurl. A t–r–a–y, tray.' He enunciated each letter with great deliberation.

'Oh!' was all I could muster.

'Aw, Artie, don't be like that. She looks all upset, gawd 'elp 'er, she does an' all.' Auntie Ada's fat orange fingers squeezed mine. ''E's a one an' no mistake. Always been a funny bugger, but I 'spect ya knows 'im by now, darlin', dontcha, eh?'

Yes, I know him by now, Auntie Ada. As my brothers would have said he's what begins with a 'b' and ends in 'd'. Bastard! That's what he is, and one day, Auntie Ada, one day, if I find them all again, then Auntie Ada we'll . . .

The thought of my family made the ache in my chest rise swiftly to my throat, and I took the teapots and hot-water jug into the kitchen. The tears spilled down my cheeks and I brushed them away angrily. I was glad to be doing the washing and wiping, and when the ache in my throat became unbearable, I sobbed, no longer wanting to stanch the flow of anger and grief that I felt. It had become strange but true that once I succumbed to the grief and the swirling tides of unhappiness I felt, my tears dried more quickly. I splashed cold water on to my face and patted it dry with a tea towel.

My breathing became even again and I knelt down where Blimp was curled in his basket. He licked my face and I felt that even he could sense my unhappiness. Sporadic laughter was coming from the dining-room, interspersed with soft murmurings. Rising to my feet, I turned to go up to my room, only to remember with a pang that it was now Auntie Ada's and Rosie's. Blimp jumped up. He must have heard the key turn in the front-door lock before I did and was barking as I ascended the stairs to take refuge in the bathroom. Chaos reigned once more as the dining-room door burst open and Rosie came clattering out. Above the dog's bark and the noise from the other adults, Rosie's voice rang out, 'Go-Go, Go-Go!'

I watched from the stairs as this great lumbering woman, her pendulous breasts and enormous buttocks encased in a clinging red woollen dress, threw her arms around Gordon. I stayed on those shaking stairtreads only to watch Gordon's hand steady him on the wall, while Rosie's incredibly slim legs, encased in nylon stockings with black seams and fluffy pink backless mules, kicked upwards towards the huge mass of her fleshy posterior, thus placing her full weight on Gordon. I waited for the crash, but none came, only Gordon's voice, muffled at first and then louder, 'Oh, Christ, get off me, Rosie! Rosie, I mean it. Leave it out, you stupid bitch, Kee – rist! Ma, will you get –?'

'Aw, Go-Go! Go-Go, don't be so bleedin' rotten.'

Those were the last words I heard as I closed the bathroom door.

Later that afternoon I went over to Pauline's with her present. Her parents were out – it was the busiest time of the year for them she said. I told her about Auntie Ada and Rosie. 'Ignore her, silly fat cow,' was Pauline's advice. Pauline asked if I'd had any Christmas cards from my family yet, and when I said I hadn't, she told me sagely that 'fosties' never do usually and began to cry, so I ended up comforting her. She took a bottle of Stone's Ginger Wine out of the sideboard cupboard and poured some into two cups, and we toasted ourselves to a happy Christmas, burning our throats and making our eyes water before I left to spend my first 'fosty' Christmas.

10

I was feeling slightly light-headed from the ginger wine when I returned, to find Mrs Oakes and Auntie Ada preparing shepherd's pie for dinner. The kitchen was warm and so was Auntie Ada's greeting.

''Ere she is, Kaff. Nice cuppa coffee, eh, warm the cockles of yer 'art, eh?'

'Yes, thank you, Auntie. I'll make it.'

'Nah, you go an' sit in the front room. Fire's burning a treat. Rosie's in there an' Artie. I was makin' fer them, go on.'

Rosie was lying across the settee reading *Woman* magazine, while her uncle was cleaning records with a new record-cleaning wonder-gadget purchased, again, at the Ideal Home Exhibition. He looked up as I came into the lounge and spoke in a soft voice.

''Ello, seen your friend, eh?'

'Yes.'

He returned to the job in hand, and I wondered if he was being nice because Auntie Ada had told him off about the tray business earlier. Rosie didn't look up but continued to leaf through the magazine. The only sound that broke the silence was the crisp slicing noise as she flicked the pages. I sat down in one of the armchairs and gazed into the dancing flames of the fire.

Auntie Ada came in bearing a t–r–a–y of steaming

mugs of coffee. ''Ere we go, darlin', git on the outside o' that.' She handed me a blue-and-white striped mug. I smiled up at her and thanked the moving dentures.

As it had become apparent that this was the room where Christmas was celebrated, I wondered whether I'd have to stay up until midnight or even later until they vacated it so that I could go to bed on the settee on which Rosie was now reposing. During dinner, however, Mrs Oakes announced that they'd all have to go into the dining-room and borrow Gordon's portable record-player so that I could go to bed at ten o'clock. Tomorrow night would be a late one, she warned, as the Knightleys always came for Christmas Eve.

Rosie became boisterous again as the meal progressed and, for Gordon's benefit, repeated the conundrum his father had set me at lunch-time. 'She couldn't git it tho', Go-Go, could ya?' She nudged my arm and nearly sent me flying backwards through the french windows.

''Ere, careful, Rosie gel, ya don't know yer own strength. You OK darlin'?' Auntie Ada inquired. I wriggled about in my chair to show that I was quite secure and in no danger, although my cheeks burned again and I couldn't bring myself to look up at any of them.

'OK, Rose, I know something that you'll never get. It begins with "m" and ends in "d".' It was Gordon who was speaking.

'Oh, Go-Go, 'ang on, I'll get it. Mad, morbid, uh ... messed about?' She clapped her enormous hands together and guffawed at the wit of her third guess.

'No, Rose, married, m–a–r–r–i–e–d,' said Gordon, and scraping back his chair, he left the table.

'Now then, Gor–don!' His mother rose to her feet and followed him out of the dining-room. Still I remained with my head bowed, as I heard Rosie and her mother both light their cigarettes and saw the first shimmer of blue-grey smoke hover over the table.

'Ooh, them two's always been like this, ain't they, Artie? Oi, darlin', 'tain't meant ya know.' She was obviously addressing me, and I looked up through the smoke at the orangey-white hue that was Auntie Ada and smiled. I still felt guilty, as though I had caused this rift between the cousins, and Rosie's next words reinforced that guilt.

''E's a right bleedin' pig, 'e is, an' I 'ate 'im! 'E's only showing off 'cos she –' Rosie broke off in mid-sentence and pushed back her chair. The floorboards groaned as she ran out of the room and clambered noisily up the stairs to 'my' bedroom, where a loud crunch suggested that she'd thrown herself on 'my' bed.

Mrs Oakes reappeared looking flustered.

'I was jest sayin', always been the same them two, wiv their bickerin', ain't they, Kaff, ever since they was little 'uns. 'Tain't meant, though. They'll 'ave made it up in a minute. Ain't I right, eh?'

The Oakeses both agreed with Auntie Ada wholeheartedly. All three of them had got used to their kids' fights. I wondered how they could call their offspring 'kids' when Gordon's hair was completely grey and Rosie's hair was turning grey too.

After I'd helped Mrs Oakes and Auntie Ada wash up, I asked if I could get ready for bed. They insisted that I go and get my things and have a good night's sleep. Both Mrs Oakes and Auntie Ada kissed me goodnight. Mr Oakes, standing in the doorway of the kitchen, proffered his cheek and said 'Night, night.'

I giggled to myself over Gordon's wisecrack at Rosie's

expense. Gordon had well and truly gone up in my estimation, and even Mr Oakes had been, well, not exactly friendly, but better somehow. Mrs Oakes and Auntie Ada had been really nice. I went up the stairs feeling happier than I had in a long time.

As I started taking my pillow and bedlinen from the top shelf of the airing cupboard I was surprised to see wrapped Christmas presents on some of the shelves. I took my pyjamas and dressing-gown from the big box and, swearing softly, picked up some of my socks and underwear that had fallen on to the floor of the airing cupboard. Carrying the huge bundle of bedding and nightclothes, I made my way gingerly down the stairs and into the lounge.

The lights were off and the red glow of the fire was welcoming and cosy, its reflection spun on the silver and coloured baubles on the Christmas tree. I was going to enjoy my stay in the lounge over Christmas and I thought spitefully that Rosie wouldn't like it if she knew; it would be folly to let her find out, as she would surely want me to go and sleep with Auntie Ada. I chuckled to myself as I thought about Gordon's riddle again and began to hum the catchy song that Mrs Oakes always sang when she was happy: 'Everything's in Rhythm with My Heart'. As I spread the last blanket over the settee the rhythm of my heart seemed to miss a beat. My socks, vests, and pants had been on the floor of the airing cupboard and I'd put them all back into my big box. My little box had held them and the kitten box — had it been there?

I ran upstairs. Frantically I searched through that cupboard. Sheets, pillowslips, bolster cases, towels, the Christmas presents. Old faded blankets and even two

97

discoloured and torn old pillows came under my scrutiny, but my little box had vanished, and with it the kitten box. Oh God, who could have taken it? Nothing could replace Mummy's scarf, the lock of her black silky hair or my Mabel Lucie Attwell annual. They were all I had of her and now they were gone. I made my way downstairs to my new 'bedroom'. The warm glow of the fire had become a flickering orange flame that reached out to scorch my very soul, as it did whenever I remembered what my father had told me, that I had caused Mummy's death. Maybe the spirit world had taken the box from me, the mediums who used to give my father messages from Mummy. No living person would want to take my kitten box. I began to tremble with fear and, getting into my makeshift bed, turned on my side and buried my head in the back of the settee, lest the glow from the embers bring back the ghost of Christmas past with Daddy.

I hadn't undressed and my tears fell for a long, long time. Only 363 days ago I had been with the boys and my baby sister and my father. I tried to count back the days since I'd seen my mother, 500 and something, and again the orange candle glowed until my tears extinguished its light and I fell exhausted into the darkness of slumber.

The cold, bluey clear morning air and its darkness usually shrouded my sorrow and was strangely comforting. I would do my round while I churned over my thoughts and memories. This time was my time. The heavy old black bike that had belonged to a retired midwife (I'd borrowed the five pounds she had asked for it from Mr Oakes and had long since repaid the loan) was my trusty steed. The few early risers I'd meet regularly on my round would often gauge how late or early I was as they made their way to catch the early train to London or walked their dogs. These people had become my friends. We had a common bond in this, our early morning time, and often exchanged pleasantries. One old lady would saunter to her gate and wait for me in all weathers. I had promised her that I would go in one day for a cup of tea. This morning I had felt guilty when she had given me a squashy, badly wrapped present and bade me have a very happy Christmas. Suspecting that I would be sent into the town for some last-minute shopping during the day, I resolved to buy her a card and a small box of chocolates and pop into her house with them. She was very frail and reminded me of Granny. I wondered if there would be a card from Gran, but my hopes were dwindling fast now.

This Christmas Eve morning there were many more people about than usual, but my mind was preoccupied with my missing kitten box. The sinister thoughts of last night – a ghostly hand being responsible for its disappearance – had vanished with the morning's scramble to get the bedclothes folded and put into the airing cupboard, of which I had made another swift search but to no avail. Mr Taylor had remarked on how puffy my eyes were and proclaimed that I must have slept heavily or had styes coming. I had agreed to both possibilities as I'd folded and stacked my papers into the canvas bag.

When I got back to the shop to collect my wages after my paper round, I impulsively bought a box of chocolate liqueurs for Auntie Ada, a box of Newberry Fruits for Mr and Mrs Knightley, and five chocolate Father Christmases wrapped in red and silver foil. I would hang them on the Christmas tree that night. Mr

Taylor gave me an extra five shillings as a Christmas-box, which meant I had just over three pounds savings even after I'd made my purchases.

My chest still felt heavy, and my eyes pricked as I tried to imagine what the boys and Anna would be doing on this special day. I wondered if they would think of me and a sigh escaped from the depth of my very being as I put the bike away inside the garage.

I could smell bacon and eggs frying as I came up the garden path and into the warmth of the kitchen. Mrs Oakes was in the kitchen looking flustered, still in her dressing-gown with a scarf wrapped around her head. I suspected that it was her one concession to her visitors that her curlers were camouflaged.

'It's cold this morning, really bitter. I brought the *Daily Herald*, I couldn't –'

'Listen to me, young lady,' she interrupted and, waving a fish slice in my direction, began an admonishment I wasn't expecting. 'Dads's after your tail, miss,' she snapped.

I supposed that was an improvement on my top-end! 'What have –'

'Leaving your bloody bedding all over the lounge floor, that's what, young lady. Shit!' Bacon fat had spat at her from the frying-pan and she rubbed angrily at her cheek. 'That room is special at Christmas, and we like to keep it tidy.'

'But I did put it away, honestly.'

'Some of it maybe, but you dropped a blanket on the floor and your nightclothes was left draped across the armchair. What you got in that bag and whose been givin' you presents, eh?'

'I bought Mr and Mrs Knightley some Newberry

Fruits, and this' – the holly-printed paper was now gaping open, revealing red woollen mittens – 'is a present from an old lady on Symonds Avenue I deliver to.'

This news seemed to placate her somewhat and she handed me a cup of hot tea. 'Dads's really mad about those bedclothes, mind, and a right old mess you've made in that airing cupboard too! If Auntie Ada and Rosie are thoughtful enough to go buying you presents, you've got no business snooping around, and I don't mean maybe! Now then d'you want this eggs and bacon or just toast.'

'Just toast thanks, and I'm sorry.'

'You're sorry! Sorry don't cost anything, my girl. A little bit of thought for others is better than bloody sorry.'

'Sorry,' I repeated as I made my way into the dining-room with my cup of tea and the newspaper.

'Sorry,' I repeated nervously as I handed Mr Oakes the *Daily Herald.* He looked up and grunted as he took the newspaper from my hand. Rosie was the only other person sitting at the dining-table, painting her ugly nails a pretty orange colour. Evidence that Gordon, Auntie Ada, Rosie and Mr Oakes had partaken of a cooked breakfast was stacked in the middle of the table.

Mr Oakes quickly opened the newspaper and Rosie opened her mouth to receive a piece of toast thickly spread with her aunt's home-made lemon curd. She crunched noisily and intermittently blew on her huge right hand and shook it, the great fingers splaying like a large fan, to dry the varnish. I collected the pile of greasy plates and took them out to the kitchen. Mrs Oakes's smile made me wonder if she was more angry with Rosie painting her nails and not clearing the table than she was with me, but she said nothing as I placed the plates into the sink to be washed and took a tray to collect the side plates and cups and saucers strewn about the dining-table. Mrs Oakes placed her plate of eggs and bacon where Gordon usually sat. The smell of nail varnish and the blue smoke that was billowing from the green glass ashtray in front of Rosie meant that I was going to have smoked toast and like it. I squeezed past her chair to get to my place at the top of the table. As I sat down, Rosie picked up her cigarette and blew a perfect smoke ring in the air.

''Ere, if ya wanna know what Fahver Christmas is bringin' ya, ya orta learn ter wait instead o' goin' through me Mum's and me's presents like ya did.'

On that note Rosie began to adorn yet another piece of toast with lemon curd. Oranges and lemons I thought, as I watched the orange nails grip the lemon-topped toast. I picked up my knife . . . *here comes a chopper to chop off your head, Rosie . . .* and took a piece of toast. How I hated this gross woman with her black, slug-like eyebrows, her eyes puffy from sleep and teeth that without the contrast of the crimson lipstick looked only three or four shades lighter than the thick yellow spread she was munching.

I waited for Mr Oakes to join Rosie in her jibes as she began to hold forth again about not liking nosey people, but he didn't refer to the subject then or ever.

''Ello, young 'un.'

'Hello, Auntie.' I was waiting for her to tell me off about the devastation in the airing cupboard and wondered what form a telling off from Auntie Ada would take. Instead she insisted that me and Kaff 'ave a nice hot cuppa 'cos ours 'ad gorn cold.

'Fire's caught luvly in the front room, Artie. I'll give this bugger a gee up when I've done the coffee; 'ave 'im goin' like a good 'un an' all.' She pushed back her white and amber hair, leaving soot smudges on her cheek and forehead as if to emphasize the point.

She'd been speaking to her brother-in-law in a strange whistling way. Studying her more closely as she stood gazing above my head out of the french windows, I saw that her mouth resembled that of an anteater I'd seen once at the zoo. Her hair was twisted into different shapes by what looked to be hundreds of white sheep grazing amongst the sand dunes of her snowcapped hair. Suddenly her eyes lowered to mine and lifted again in a smile.

'Lorst all me gnashers 'avin 'er.' She inclined the grazing sheep towards her daughter, who was, incredibly, still munching. It was my opinion that Auntie Ada had lorst more than 'er gnashers 'avin 'er. Poor Auntie Ada was no winner in the offspring stakes, that was certain.

She reached over to take one of Rosie's cigarettes and matches, lit up and resumed her position in front of the dining-room fire, her gaze once more above my head. A smell began to pervade the room, a smell that overpowered that of bacon and eggs, nail varnish, acetone and cigarette smoke. It was the cloying smell of stale urine and it seemed to be getting stronger by the second, expanding in the enclosed room. I started to get up, not wanting any more comments on my personal hygiene from Mrs Oakes. As I stood up I saw that Auntie Ada had hoisted up her brown skirt at the back to warm her bottom, exposing a vast expanse of pink bloomers. The cigarette was hanging from her lips and I watched briefly as it moved in and out of the black void of her mouth, expecting it to disappear as her cheeks expanded and contracted rythmically. Both hands were still clutching the skirt. Oblivious to her surroundings, she stood there, smoke encompassing her face and head, her eyes shut against the acrid fumes. Suddenly she released the hold on her skirt and, with one last suck, retrieved the minute fag end deftly with thumb and forefinger, and threw it on to the sluggish fire.

'Now then, I were gonna get some coffee, weren't I, eh?'

'I'll give you a hand, Auntie.' The smell was making my throat sore. Everyone seemed to decide to move at once, except for Rosie, who still languished in her chair.

'C'mon, lady muck, gimme a 'and wiv these dishes an' the coffee. Up orf yer arse – ooh, pardon me French.' Auntie Ada placed a black and tan hand over her toothless mouth and whistled a giggle.

'I'll wash up, Auntie, while you wash your hands,' I laughed.

'Yes, go on, Ada luvvy, have a little wash. The water's hot in the bathroom.' Mrs Oakes shooed her up the stairs. 'Right then, Rosie, you can dry up and put away while I make some coffee, and don't think you're sittin' there with your nose in the paper all morning, Artie. You can make that fire up . . . and open them french doors, and I don't mean maybe.'

'Aw, Auntie!' Rosie protested.

'Now, Rosie, this bloody minute!' Mrs Oakes threw a tea towel at her. A look of shock passed over Rosie's face as she slowly got up from her chair staring at the tea towel.

'I'll chip me nails,' she wailed.

Mrs Oakes raised her eyes to the heavens and back to mine, gave me a conspiratorial wink and squeezed my arm.

Later that day Mrs Oakes sent me up to what had been my bedroom to return a selection of shoes, scarves, nail polishes and lipsticks Rosie'd left lying around the lounge: Mr and Mrs Knightley were coming tonight, Rosie was an untidy, lazy lump and we'd have to see if we could keep her out of the lounge until the Knightleys arrived. I'd felt very privileged when Mrs Oakes had imparted this information to me, and the fact that she had given me the responsibility of taking care of Rosie's untidiness gave me a sense of importance in this home that I'd never had before. Now, opening the door, I was shocked at the untidiness, and the chaos assaulting my eyes made me wonder if I should report the matter.

Making my way across the items of clothing on the floor to Rosie's bed, I placed the lipstick and nail varnish amongst the debris covering the dressing-table. I was putting her shoes by the side of the bed when I noticed something pink lying on top of a large salmon-coloured corset. My throat constricted as I realized it was Mummy's scarf, and with an audible cry I picked up the soft pink chiffon and held it to my nose and mouth. Slewed at a drunken angle at the foot of the bed was the kitten box. My heart was hammering as I ran and grasped it. It was empty. The envelope with Mummy's lock of hair was gone, as was the annual. I began to look around the room, not knowing where to begin. The book was large enough to be easily seen, but the black-rimmed envelope my father had given me would take some searching for.

'Oh yeah?' Rosie's voice made me jump. I hadn't heard her come into the room.

'It's my –' I began.

'Yeah, your room was ya gonna say, eh?'

'No, it's my . . .'

'Sid down an' I'll tell ya summit. Go on, sit on me ol' dear's bed if ya can find room.'

I did as I was told, still clutching the kitten box and the scarf.

'I'm tellin' ya this so ya'll git the picture, like. This ain't no more your room than it's mine, see?' I didn't, but let Rosie continue. 'Well, it's like everythin' wiv Auntie Kaff, Unc an' Go-Go. Ever see them cages they got down the garridge?' I shook my head. 'Well, they tried t' breed canaries once. I bet ya Auntie Kaff has showed ya the weddin' dress she made fer that silly tart Go-Go took up wiv. She 'as, ain't she?' I nodded. 'Tell ya she made it an' all, I bet. Well, she didn', see! That were bought in Bon Marches in the West End, but she 'as all the bleedin' brides in the district ringin' 'er up once she's put an ad in the local an' they sees it. All wants one jest like it wevver they was gettin' married or not, I reckon. 'Ad orders fer seven, she did, an' five didn' bovver to turn up fer fittins an' the satisfied two knocked 'er down in price an' all!'

She was picking matted pieces of wool from her dark-blue dressing-gown and dropping them on to the floor. A slight ripping sound broke through the silence at each pinch of the cloth. Two buttons were missing from the dressing-gown and the short nightdress she was wearing had obviously been made by Mrs Oakes. Her slim white legs were covered in short black hairs, and the white fur of the mules and black fur of exposed leg made her look like a Walt Disney character. I was about to tell her that I believed that Mrs Oakes had made the wedding dress when she put up a large hand to silence me.

"'Ang on a mo!' She splayed out her huge orange-tipped fingers and struck the little finger of her left hand with the index finger of her right. I watched in fascination. 'I've said about the weddin' dresses, that's one.' She struck her ring finger. 'Then Uncle Artie was gonna make a mint breedin' Labradors – 'ad about fourteen of 'em at one time. Christ, ya shoulda' been 'ere then, kid.' She pinched her long nose. 'Phew, wotta ronk! An' then there were one, poor ol' Blimp.' She struck her middle finger. 'Then Auntie Kaff decided on breedin' them Siamese cats, Chocolate Points, Coffee Points, Seal Points, Blue Points, even bleedin' pencil points I shouldn' be surprised!' At this quip she screamed with laughter.

Not knowing anything about Siamese cats, I failed to find this amusing. In fact, I was at a loss to understand why she was telling me all this. All I wanted to do was to get my book and the envelope and hide them where no one in the world could ever find them again. I was about to get up when she began holding forth again.

"'Ere, ya orta wise-up kid, an' if ya don't believe me, just go an' take a butchers down the garridge. 'Ere, ain't Artie ever showed ya none of 'is inventions then? Christ, there's everyfing down there except a bleedin' spaceship – I'm speakin' too soon; 'e's probably got one o' them an' all plugged in by now!' This produced further guffaws of laughter.

She lit a cigarette and threw the spent match on the glass-topped dressing-table. I felt my heart skip a beat as she suddenly jumped up and came to sit beside me on her mother's bed. The mattress springs protested, causing me to see-saw upwards as she sat down.

'Then there's Go-Go, oh gawd blimey, Go-Go!' I

watched index finger strike index finger. 'Old coins 'e were into. Runnin' about all over London, even came an' stayed wiv me an' me mum once 'cos there were an auction or somethin'. Gold sovereigns out o' the *Exchange an' Mart*. 'Ere, 'e even went down t' Cornwall once fer some Elizabef the first duckets or some such bleedin' rubbish.'

I watched as the thumb was struck and her eyes narrowed against the smoke.

'Now we got 'Itler!'

'Who's that?' I spoke for the first time in what seemed like hours.

' 'Itler. Ya don' know who Adolf 'Itler is?'

'Oh yes, of course I do.'

'Well, 'e's really inta 'im in a big way. 'E's got German 'elmets, boots, knives, guns, all them Nazi flags an' fings. 'Ere, kid, ask 'im anyfing ya wanna about Adolf 'Itler an' 'e'll tell ya if 'e were bleedin' constipated or no, straight up 'e will!' More guffaws of laughter.

By now the ash from the cigarette was in a pyramid-shaped pile on the dressing-table and I watched, amazed, as Rosie crushed the cigarette into the top, making it look like a miniature volcano. She lit another cigarette and I sensed that her mood had become more serious. Perhaps she was coming to the point of this rather strange conversation. Again I was filled with apprehension, but she spoke quietly.

' 'E's a swine, 'e is, fer collectin' fings like that. My dad was killed in the war, ya know, an' if ya fink about it, one o' them bleedin' knives or guns 'e's got in that room of 'is could be the very one that them Nazi bastards killed me dad wiv. Well, they could, could'n' they? Don' ya go tellin' me mum what 'e collects now, she'd 'ave a bleedin' fit, she would an' all!'

I promised not to tell as Rosie crushed another cigarette end into the swirling pile of grey ash.

'I remember me dad. 'E was big an' tall an' ever so 'andsome, wiv my black curly 'air.' She ran her fingers through her artificial curls to emphasize the point, her black, slug-like eyebrows embracing briefly as she frowned. I'd seen some some grey photographs of John, her father, with Arthur and Kathleen Oakes and Auntie Ada. He looked at least a foot shorter than Auntie in the photographs, even shorter than his younger brother, Artie. His hair was dark and formed a V shape at either side of his head. The silence that had now fallen made me feel obliged to say something sympathetic about Rosie's dad.

'I'm sorry about your dad being –'

'Oh Christ, that were bleedin' years ago now, but you, you ain't understood nuffin' I've been tryin' t' tell ya, 'ave ya, eh?'

'I have, I've been listening to everything you've said.' The blood rushed to my cheeks and I got up off the bed while Rosie lit yet another cigarette and tossed another match on to the dressing-table.

'Listen 'ere, you. I'm tellin' ya this fer yer own bleedin' good, not fer mine, so don' git all uppity wiv me. Yer just anuvver 'obby t' them, like Artie wiv 'is Labradors an' Kaff wiv er Siameses an' weddin' dresses, an' Go-Go wiv 'is funny bleedin' cars an' coins an' German war stuff. D'ya git me drift, eh? Oh, an' the canaries – I did say about them, didn' I? 'Obbies, that's all they are, only they ain't 'ad a 'uman one before, see?'

An uncontrollable trembling shook my body.

'Aw Christ, come on, don' start blubbin', fer gawd's sakes. 'Ave a fag, 'ere, go on.'

My head swayed from side to side with uncontrollable trembling. I had to get away from this room, this woman and all the awful things she'd said. Clutching my kitten box and the scarf, I made for the door.

'Eh, where ya goin' wiv that box? I've bagged that!' She reached across and tore it from my grasp.

'No, no, it's mine!'

'Who says?'

'Your Auntie Kath, she gave it to me, it was to put my private things in, they were mine.' My voice was raised and deep, ugly sobs came from my throat. I saw a flicker of fear and sudden comprehension dawn in her brown eyes.

'Wot, ya mean yer book an' that tatty ol' pink scarf? Ya don' honestly fink I'd nick them, do ya? Well, do ya? 'Ang on a mo, 'ere's yer bleedin' book!' She shuffled under some magazines and retrieved it from beside her bed. 'I wants that box, though. I was gonna put all these in fer Kaff. They're 'er favourite Lilies of the Valley an' they sold out o' the presentation boxes. I was gonna line that wiv pretty paper and give 'er these.' She tipped a Timothy White's bag on to her bed, tumbling out an assortment of talcum powder, bath salts, bath cubes, soaps, cologne and matching perfume. 'Good idea, yeah?'

I nodded. 'Did you find an envelope in the box?' I asked, realizing I had to concede defeat over the kitten box.

'Yeah! One wiv black edges. It's round 'ere somewhere. Christ, that ain't yours, is it? Ya don' wannit, do ya?' I nodded. 'It's round 'ere somewhere. 'Ang about, where's me bleedin' cards. I got Go-Go a book token so's 'e can buy 'isself a book about 'Itler an' concentration camps or somethin' cheerful like that! 'Ere it is!' She had retrieved my envelope from a pile of Christmas cards scattered on her pillow. 'Look, I put some o' them German zeds on it fer a laugh!'

The envelope fell from her hand and we both dived to pick it up.

'Git orf!' Rosie exclaimed as the envelope landed in the cup of the largest brassiere I had ever seen.

I was too swift for her and retrieved it. The black-edged envelope in which my father had placed the precious lock was now etched with poorly drawn swastikas, and a childish hand had scrawled 'From one Germ to another, love from Rosie'. Crosses were drawn on the bottom of the envelope. As Rosie's hand reached out to grab the envelope, the lock of black hair fell out on to a white petticoat lying among the debris of clothing. Rosie held the envelope firmly in her grasp while I bent to pick up the black silky hair, which looked almost like a question mark. Rosie's interest became acute.

'What's that then, eh? 'Ere, let's 'ave a gander. What is it? There weren't nuffin' in that envelope when I wrote on it fer Go-Go. Give it 'ere!'

'No! It's mine! Don't you dare touch it, Rosie. It's mine!'

''Air, that's what it is, 'air,' she repeated in amazement.

'It's mine!' I repeated, more vehemently now.

'Yers? Yers?' Rosie screeched with laughter. 'Christ, I'd better check!' Rosie parted her thick black and white legs and, lifting her dressing-gown and nightie above her knees, bent her head in a pretence of examining her pubic area. Her huge frame convulsed with laughter as at last she straightened herself upright. 'It bloody well must be. Gawd's streuth, I thought fer a minute I was bleedin' moltin'!' More screams of laughter issued from Rosie's mouth. Her face had turned purple.

'Wotcha makin' all this din fer, Rosie? Gawd, ya ain't even dressed yet, ya lazy bitch, an' just look at the state o' this room, bleedin' 'ell!'

Neither Rosie nor myself had heard her mother come into the room. I looked up and saw Mrs Oakes standing behind Auntie Ada. She came round in front of her sister-in-law and stared in disbelief at the carnage all round her. She clasped her hand across her mouth as she saw the mound Rosie had made with her cigarette ends and ash.

'Look here, Rosie, you're not leaving everything to your Mum and me this year. It is Christmas Eve, you know!' Mrs Oakes's face was white with anger and her hands were trembling.

'Ooh, don' look, Auntie Kaff!' Rosie squealed.

'You're a bit late, Rosie. I already have and it's bloody disgraceful. The room's like a pigsty and the Knightleys are coming this evening!'

'Aw, I don' mean the mess, Auntie, I don' want ya t' see yer presents I mean. 'Ide yer eyes, Auntie Kaff, go on.' Rosie was trying to conceal the toiletries spread over the bed by pulling garments up from the floor and draping them over the packages and bottles.

Mrs Oakes ignored Rosie and turned her attention to me. 'What's happened to your box, ducks, eh?'

'She says I can 'ave it, did'n' ya?'

I nodded.

''Ere, ain't that the . . .?' Auntie Ada's question hung in the air. Mrs Oakes must have affirmed that it was and must have told Auntie Ada about the box and its contents. 'Give that littl'un 'er box back, Rosie, now, right now or ya'll be fer it, gel, an' I ain't waitin'!' Auntie Ada's voice was low and threatening. In fact, she didn't even sound like Auntie Ada, which scared me.

'But she says I can 'ave –'

'I don' care wot she says. Give it an' git your cloves and git dressed, in that barfroom now, an' don' you come the ol' acid wiv me, bleedin' well git!'

Rosie was furious. Each step she took made the room shudder, as with slow deliberation she picked up the enormous brassiere, the salmon-pink corset, nylon stockings and the red woollen dress. She nearly tripped over the pink fluffy mules she'd been wearing last night.

'Fuckin' 'ell!' She kicked at the pretty pink slippers.

'Wash yer mawf out wiv soda while yer in the barfroom,' Auntie Ada instructed her as Rosie swaggered out of the room.

'I didn' wan' 'er fuckin' box anyways. Ya can shove it!' were Rosie's parting words as she slammed the bathroom door, leaving me feeling guilty about reclaiming the box.

Auntie Ada, whose teeth has been reinstated since I'd seen her earlier, teeth that had clicked and clacked like a machine gun during her attack on Rosie, now seemed also to surrender. The orange and white teeth fell on to the carpet, looking like pastry cutters. One long gleaming strand of spittle stretched from Auntie's mouth to the pastry cutters, an umbilicus as delicate as a spider's web, which broke as she addressed me.

'You all right, darlin'?'

I was trying hard not to show that my hands were still shaking. The lock of hair felt coarse and damp with the perspiration from my clenched hand.

'You jist git yer box an' yer bits, an' don' 'ave no more truck wiv 'er, d'ya 'ear me? Yer t' tell yer ol' Auntie if she tries t' come it agin.' She whistled. It was then that she bent down, wiped fluff from her pastry cutters' and, with a further clacking sound, put them back in her mouth.

'Don't you do the room, Ada, let her, and I don't mean maybe!' Mrs Oakes advised her sister-in-law.

'Too bleedin' true I won't, Kaff. She's gotta learn!'

Auntie Ada and Mrs Oakes left the room. Auntie Ada rapped on the bathroom door and told her daughter she wanted her 'out o' the barfroom in five minutes an' the bedroom tidied in a 'alf 'our or there'd be bleedin' trouble!' Picking up the kitten box and putting the scarf and annual inside, I peeled the strand of Mummy's hair from my palm and placed it on top of the scarf. I'd have to find another envelope. I put the lid on the box and made my exit from the bedroom too.

'Happy bloody Christmas this is,' I heard Gordon shout to no one in particular as I went down the stairs. He was just emerging from his room and must have heard all the fuss. I went into the lounge and found some used Christmas-card envelopes on top of the radiogram. Picking up one, I opened the kitten box, placed the lock of hair inside the envelope and pushed the box under the settee as far as it would go.

Lunch was a sombre affair and afterwards I was sent to the greengrocer to get dates and figs and a pound of walnuts that had not arrived with Mrs Oakes's order. Once again she'd been on the telephone giving a tradesman a 'piece of her mind'. It was as I rode to the town that I absorbed the full impact of what Rosie had said about the crushes that her uncle, aunt and cousin had

had on different things. Well, they seemed like crushes to me, like Pauline and some of the girls had on Elvis, Tab Hunter or Tommy Steele.

I pushed the bike along to Taylor's, where I bought a Christmas card and a Dairy Box for the old lady on Symonds Avenue. Mr Taylor let me write the card in the shop, and when I handed it and the chocolates to the old lady, she begged me to come in. I promised to do so on Boxing Day. She had tears in her eyes as she opened the card and clutched at my hand with her tiny bird-like delicate one. I didn't want to stay in case she told me she would be alone on Christmas Day, but, looking at the wedding ring now grown too large for her tiny finger, I told myself that she'd have her children visiting. She kissed my cheek and asked God to bless me. I sent up a prayer that God would not let her or anyone say anything kind to me; I was a 'fosty', a hobby, and I knew that I was being punished.

It was beginning to grow dark as I pushed the black bike out of the old lady's gate. I wanted the darkness, wanted it to envelop me, to take me to my own world, where Daddy would be in one of his good moods and Granny would be sitting in the kitchen drinking tea and smoking her Weights or Woodbines, the boys would be laughing and excited and little Anna would be taking her faltering steps to Mummy's outstretched arms. Mummy! My very soul wanted to scream for her to come, come back.

The orange candle's flame flared, burning my soul as it licked through my mind: remember you knocked her head and then she was dead, it hissed. I rode fast down Symonds Avenue, my face turned upwards to the biting cold wind.

11

Bert Knightley and his wife, Marion, had arrived. 'Bert the Bobby' Rosie called him. Rosie seemed to be a different person. We were in the kitchen making mince pies, and she confided in me that Bert 'fancied her rotten' – I thought his fancy to be a true assessment of her – and had wanted to go out with her for ages.

The smell of the mince pies baking, mixed with the scent of tangerines and pine-needles, carried me away from a world where, for Rosie, romance lay with Bert the Bobby, back to *my* world and a sudden vision of lemonade, cordials, tonic water and a thick frosted-glass soda siphon like the empty one my brothers and I had once stolen from the back of a lorry for a dare . . . How could I rid myself of these memories, I wondered a hundred times that day, a hundred aspirins' worth.

I fought back the tears and returned to the sound of Rosie's voice and this world, where the sideboard in the dining-room and the radiogram in the lounge were weighed down with mountainous glass bowls of fruit, bowls of mixed nuts with nutcrackers by their sides, and trays of drinks: green bottles of Stone's Ginger Wine (which Pauline had introduced me to) and Gordon's gin, Cockburn's port, Johnnie Walker whisky, brandy and sherry and a bottle full of a thick yellow substance that Auntie Ada informed me was egg-nog.

In the lounge Auntie Ada, Mrs Knightley and Mrs Oakes were seated on the settee. Bert the Bobby was in one armchair and Mr Oakes in the other. Rosie sat on a pouffe between the two armchairs. She was heavily painted, with lips the colour of the tangerines, and wore a huge tartan dress with a lace Peter Pan collar and her furry pink mules. I noticed that her thick tartan-clad arm was resting on the side of Bert Knightley's chair. Gordon was poised on a stool next to his father's armchair. Boxes of chocolates, Turkish delight, cigarettes and cigars, and a huge table lighter I'd never seen before rested on an occasional table in front of the settee.

Mrs Oakes had asked me to put on my red-and-brown-check dress and new white socks, and she'd given me some red satin ribbon to tie in my hair. I was more than happy to play waitress, and proffered the ham sandwiches, mince pies and sausage rolls at regular intervals.

Auntie Ada sat with her legs apart, exposing stocking tops that were rolled just above her knees and met by elasticated blue bloomers, sipping port and lemon. Mrs Oakes and Mrs Knightley were sipping sherry, and I noticed that Mrs Oakes had observed her friend's drinking pace and seemed to be following suit. Rosie was drinking gin and tonic while Gordon, who was refilling the men's glasses, had joined his father and Mr Knightley in drinking beer.

'Yesh, it's been a 'ard life bein' a war widder, specially wiv our Rosie t' bring up, shtill, 'e's at peace now, my Johnny, thass the way I looks at it. Eh, Artie, d'ya remember . . .'

Auntie Ada cared nothing for the social graces her sister-in-law was observing and frequently beckoned me to fill her glass with port and lemon, eventually deciding to do without the lemon. Mrs Knightley was quickening her pace with the sherry, matched by Mrs Oakes, and Rosie had dispensed with my services and was pouring her own gin and tonic.

'My mum was a Lemmon before she got married, shpelt wiv two "m"s. Ain't that right, Mum, eh?'

Auntie Ada agreed she'd once been Ada Lemmon.

'Sho ya can squeeze me, Bert!' More guffaws of laughter from Rosie as she placed her large hand on the policeman's small knee.

'Oh, Christ, you might as well get the sharp bit over while you're at it, Rosie,' Gordon growled.

'Now then, you two, don't start. It's Christmas Eve, after all,' warned Mrs Oakes, glaring at the two cousins.

'Eh, I shay, she's sharp, I shay . . . the young 'un 'ere, ain't ya darlin? Won't say no, ta.' Auntie Ada took a mince pie and a sausage roll from the plates I held in front of her.

'What do you want to be when you leave school, luv?' Mrs Knightley inquired, waving a hand in refusal as I offered her the plates of pastries. My cheeks burned at being addressed.

Dead, Mrs Knightley, before I leave school, though, Mrs Knightley. I want to be so very, very dead, Mrs Knightley.

'I haven't decided yet,' I answered, smiling down at her.

'These mince pies are delicious. You'll have to tell the wife your secret, young Caroline.' Mr Knightley was giving me his attention now.

'He's not joking either. I can't make pastry like this, can I, Kath?'

Mrs Oakes reassured her friend that she could, but that she was very proud of me.

''Ere, git yerself a drink, darlin', eh, eh? Now, Gordon, git yer little sister a drink. Port an' lemon won' do 'er no 'arm, will it, Kaff, Bert, Artie, Marion, eh?' Auntie Ada looked around the room and everyone agreed that it would be in order.

Gordon looked at me and I averted my eyes. Gordon my brother? Me being called his sister? It seemed as distasteful to him as it did to me.

'Git the young 'un a port 'n' lemon,' Auntie Ada ordered again.

'Just lemonade, thanks,' I said.

'Go on, put a drop o' port in, son, set 'er up fer the night an' all!'

Gordon put about two inches of port in the bottom of a tumbler and topped it up with lemonade.

'That OK?' he asked, handing me the glass without looking at me. I thanked him and he moved across to replenish his mother's, aunt's and Mrs Knightley's glasses.

'Wot about me, Go-Go? 'Ere!' Rosie extended an empty glass to him.

'Haven't you had enough?' He poured her a drink anyway and she got up, weaving across the room like an armoured tank, announcing that she was 'gonna powder her nose'.

Mr Knightley and Mr Oakes had decided they'd like to switch to whisky, and as Gordon went into the kitchen for fresh glasses they began talking about the Sputnik that had been sent into space and how long it would be before the West sent up a spaceship. I wondered if Mr Oakes hadn't already patented one and had it sitting in the garage, as Rosie had suggested.

'Look at 'er little fingers when she comes over agin, an' 'er face an' 'ead, poor little soul.' Auntie Ada gave me a beaming smile, but I knew she was talking about me. ''Ere, Kaff, git 'er t' sit over 'ere wiv us, gel.'

'Go and get that beautiful yule log you made at school, luvvy,' Mrs Oakes said, smiling broadly at me.

I knew that they wanted to look more closely at the scars on my hands and face, and I automatically tugged at my fringe to hide the one on my forehead as I obediently went out to the larder to fetch the chocolate log.

I was proud of my achievement, for which Miss Lange had given me a mark of 9½, and, scars forgotten, carried it carefully into the lounge on its square silver cakeboard. I'd melted some acid drops to produce an effective display of 'ice' and had placed a robin on the glacial surface, added a snowman and a lone sprig of holly on the furrows of chocolate butter-cream, and used chocolate buttons to form notches in the log, Miss Lange had spluttered that it was 'imbressive and original and deserved the highest mark'. I wondered what you'd have to do to score the full 10 out of 10.

Oohs and aahs of genuine delight came from the three women. Mr Knightley, diverted from listening to one of Rosie's jokes, asked to see it, Gordon gave a grunt and even Mr Oakes conceded it was very good. Mr Knightley said I'd put the bakers in the town out of business. Once again my cheeks were burning, but this time with a feeling of great accomplishment. I was about to take my prize confection back to the larder when Rosie asked if she could have another 'butchers'. Her sudden squeal made me jump and nearly drop the cake, for my hands had been trembling while I'd carried it around the room.

'Oh, Bert, Unc, Auntie, Go-Go, look, look!' she screamed, pointing at the cake.

Her mother made an attempt to heave herself from the sofa, then gave up. Mrs Knightley and Mrs Oakes, however, got to their feet and came over to scrutinize the cake as if there was something they'd missed on their previous examination. Mr Knightley and Mr Oakes also gave it some attention.

'Look, look at the robin! He's ... he's peed on the log!' Rosie screamed, holding her sides with laughter, tears rolling down her face.

There was an almost audible silence as Rosie's laughter subsided, and then a sob that sounded like a chuckle escaped from my throat. I made my way out of the lounge and placed the yule log back on the larder shelf. From the kitchen I could hear John Hanson singing 'Goodbye', and them all joining in. I made the coffee and wondered how long it would be until I could say goodbye to them all, for ever.

Christmas Eve ended with Christmas carols. The final song was Rosie singing 'Chest and nuts toasting round my open fire!' I wasn't sure why her rendition of this song made her aunt order her to bed and everyone else depart so swiftly, but guessed Rosie was in disgrace. (It was a source of great amusement to Deirdre when Pauline told her about it, as it was to Pauline and me when Deirdre explained.) Mr and Mrs Oakes were saying goodbye to the Knightleys, and Auntie Ada had fallen asleep on the settee. I panicked at the thought that I'd have to spend the night in the same room as Rosie. However, after the Knightleys' departure, Mr and Mrs Oakes roused Auntie Ada and escorted her up the stairs to join her daughter in slumber.

I was washing up the last of the glasses and coffee cups when Gordon brought a glass into the kitchen.

'Leave those till the morning. You OK?' he asked gruffly.

'Yes, thanks.'

'I'll say goodnight then,' and with that he left the kitchen.

'Goodnight,' I murmured back.

Christmas Day was pure chaos. I'd never received so many presents in my life.

'Lots of smellies, luvvy, eh?' Mrs Oakes said as I sat rather bewildered by all the opened packages, and I wondered if she was really referring to my talc, bath salts and cologne or to Auntie Ada, who smelled of Ashes of Roses and urine all day. I also wondered why she hadn't introduced Auntie Ada to the world of 'day-o-dor-ants' – not as brutally of course – as she had me!

As well as the toiletries, I'd received a new dress, two jumpers, more mittens and socks, a dressing-gown with silky tassels and some chocolates from Mr and Mrs Oakes. Pauline had given me the same luminous socks as I'd given her. Even Gordon had bought me a present, a dictionary.

The turkey was the best thing I'd ever tasted, until I ate Mrs Oakes's home-made Christmas pudding; I couldn't choose between them.

The atmosphere on Boxing Day morning was a change from that of the previous two days. The flatness was lifted by Rosie's and Mr Oakes's behaviour over breakfast. I'd left the dictionary that Gordon had bought me on the sideboard and it was now open next to Rosie's plate on the table.

''E're, you learned anyfin' yet from this then, eh?'

'Yes, it's great, it really is,' I answered. Gordon cleared his throat and shifted uneasily in his chair. I could hear Auntie Ada and Mrs Oakes in the kitchen and, ill at ease with the present company, wished they'd come into the dining-room.

'Not much cop at spellin' then, are ya?' Rosie said, to which I shrugged. 'Bet ya can't spell phlegm.' Rosie was chewing her customary toast smothered with home-made lemon curd.

'Rosie, leave it out, will you?' Gordon's voice held a low warning note.

Rosie decided to ignore him. 'Ya can't, can ya? Well, can ya? I can. Begins wiv an "f", don' it, so it's "f" –'

'No it doesn't!'

'What does it begin with then, gurl?' I was surprised that Mr Oakes had decided to become party to one of Rosie's games and my heart started beating fast.

'Umm . . . "p", I think.'

Rosie was munching more toast heavily topped with more lemon curd, the texture and connotations in relation to the unfortunate choice of word they'd challenged me to spell seemingly lost on both her and her uncle.

'Come on then, gurl. "P", we've got "p". Now what comes next, um?'

'I . . . er . . . I think it's P–h–l–e–g–m,' I stammered.

'Bleedin' 'ell, I fort since I started at the chemist's I usually ketch people out wiv that 'un. They always says "Thass easy, it's f–l–e–m." Clever little bugger, ain't ya? Don' git big 'eaded, though,' she warned.

'You two are excremental, do you know that?' Gordon got up pushing his chair violently away. Mr Oakes and Rosie looked at each other, and Rosie put her tongue out as Gordon strode out of the room muttering something that I didn't hear.

'Now then, son, we were only –'

Gordon closed the dining-room door with a resounding bang.

'Wot's eatin' 'im this mornin'?' Rosie looked from her uncle to me, and we both shrugged. I decided I must look up 'excremental' in the dictionary.

Boxing Day afternoon I called to see Mrs Jennings, the old lady who lived on Symonds Avenue. She was so delighted to see me that her tiny frame seemed to glow with pleasure. She told me how wonderful her Christmas Day had been, and I was happy to learn that she had spent it with her son and daughter-in-law and three married granddaughters. It was with great pride that she showed me photographs of them, and her tiny hands shook as she fetched me a photograph of her first great-grandson, whom she'd met for the first time the day before. Her other son lived in the Far East, and her husband had been dead for three years – 'The pain never goes you know, it only lessens somewhat with time,' she told me. She would have been shocked if she'd known how familiar I was with this pain and dismayed perhaps that in my view time did not diminish it.

I bade her farewell and then called on the Knightleys with the box of Newberry Fruits. Here I was given another welcome and my second cup of tea in less than an hour. Mrs Knightley confided that neither she nor her husband could ever understand why my 'parents' stood having Auntie Ada and that awful Rosie at their house nearly every summer and every Christmas since they'd known them. I wondered if Mrs Knightley was really speaking for her husband too. He had seemed to enjoy Rosie's company on Christmas Eve, especially when she'd taken him upstairs to approve what she had bought Mrs Knightley for Christmas, and he hadn't seemed too put off by the long film-star kisses she'd given him in the hallway while I was in the kitchen.

12

The day after Boxing Day Auntie Ada and Rosie returned to London. I missed them, especially Auntie Ada, but I was surprised to discover that I missed Rosie too. Mr Oakes and Gordon had returned to their usual morose selves and the house was incredibly quiet. Even though my bedroom was reinstated as 'mine', it seemed to have an empty feeling about it after the second bed had been dismantled. Mrs Oakes and I set to work cleaning the room. Rosie seemed to have left behind all manner of things: stockings, hairclips, combs; even her tangerine lipstick was under one of the beds. I put it into the secret pocket in my satchel. I was relieved to be going back to school and couldn't wait to see Pauline.

Sometime towards the end of January, after Miss Crowley had made her monthly visit, I had a puncture half-way through my paper round. I steered the bike through the freezing cold streets and arrived back late. I put the bike in the garage and decided I'd have to get a puncture outfit during the lunch-hour and fix it then, as I wouldn't be able to see to repair it in the dark January evening. I was leaving the garage when I saw a brown light-switch on the wall; I'd never noticed it before, but then I'd never had a puncture either. I flicked the switch down, and jumped as the garage was bathed in a low light.

I looked round, surprised to see how large it was. To my left, along the full length of the wall, were three oblong plywood boxes with round holes cut into the wood at each end. I assumed these had once been the canaries' cages. They rested on a work bench, beneath which ran one long cage. Another cage the same length was placed at a right-angle along the garage wall. Both were fronted with wire mesh. Were these once the homes of the Labrador pups and the Siamese kittens? I knew that they were, that Rosie's story had been true, and an involuntary shiver ran down my spine. I heard the back door open and close, and quickly left the garage. Mr Oakes was striding down the path.

'What you been doing in there all this time, gurl? It's gone half past eight, you know.'

'I've got a puncture in my tyre,' I told him truthfully.

'Well, there's a puncture outfit in the house, cupboard under the stairs,' he informed me abruptly. 'Hey, you've left the damned light on!'

Walking into the garage with me, he pressed a thumb into the front tyre. It deflated even further and he gave a satisfied grunt. 'Gordon's off work this morning; he'll do it for you if you ask him,' he said gruffly, and walked swiftly up the path blowing on his hands.

Mrs Oakes was sympathetic when her husband confirmed that my lateness wasn't my fault, and made me a cup of Nescafé, while I ran upstairs to wash and change into my school uniform.

'Here, I've made you some toast, ducks. Now eat it and drink your coffee. You'll still make it in time.'

I smiled and thanked her and did the same to Gordon that evening when his mother informed me that he'd mended the puncture, but the discovery in the garage was gnawing away at me. I thought they might have told me about the kittens, puppies and canaries. When I eventually confided what Rosie had told me and my discovery to Pauline, she said she'd ask Deirdre. Pauline's sister reassured me that people talked about their successes, not their failures, and this dispelled my fears. Deirdre often helped me with her advice and common sense over things like this, but the major problems that I had overcome and that lay ahead were of such magnitude that I knew that not Deirdre, not anyone, not even God could help me with them.

During the first week in February I came into the kitchen and knew something was amiss. Mrs Oakes wasn't bustling around. Instead, when I looked into the dining-room, she was sitting in her chair with an opened letter in front of her.

'Listen, Kath, you've got to go, luv. We'll manage. It's got to be done and there's an end to it!' Mr Oakes had an arm around her shoulder, and I felt awkward as I took the *Daily Mail* over to the table and placed it on top of the letter that had immobilized Mrs Oakes. 'Mums has got to go into hospital for a few days; she's just had a letter,' he announced without looking up.

'Oh no!' My despair was genuine. 'Will I have to go to another home?'

'No need for that, gurl. Isn't it just like you to think about yourself instead of showing concern for Mums?' he sneered.

'Oh no, I didn't mean, I mean are you very ill?' I was shaking like a leaf.

'No, ducks. Mountains outa molehills. Just a little woman's complaint. I'll only be in for a week, that's all.'

'So it's not serious?' I asked.

'No, they take you into hospital for fun these days, gurl. She wouldn't be going –'

'Artie! There's no need for that sarcasm. She's going to be the little woman of the house and take care of my men while I'm gone, aren't you, luvvy? Iris across the road will come in to clean and Marion Knightley, well she won't see you without . . .'

'Couldn't Auntie Ada come?' I asked hopefully.

'Now you know Rosie would want to come – she'd just give her notice in at the chemist, and Auntie Ada's had a hard enough job getting her out to work as it is. She'd be more hindrance than help, and I'd only worry. No, we'll cope, luvvy, don't fret.'

A week later Mrs Oakes went into hospital. I did the cooking at night and 'prepared', as I'd been taught, in the mornings. I had to come home from school at lunch-time to feed Blimp. Iris across the road came in and 'did' for us, and each evening we'd visit Mrs Oakes. I hated the drive to the hospital, as Mr Oakes rarely spoke a word on the way there or back, but Mrs Knightley came with us twice, which made the journey pleasant. It seemed a long week, but the doctors said Mrs Oakes would be able to come home on Sunday.

Friday lunch-time, having fed Blimp, I went up to my bedroom to get some books for the afternoon's lessons. Gordon's bedroom door was ajar. I went downstairs and opened the front door, expecting to see 'Izzie' sitting there, but the little car had gone. I climbed the stairs with mounting excitement, wondering how he'd been so remiss as to leave his door unlocked. Hands shaking, I pushed the door wide open and stood on the threshold, fully expecting him to ask what the hell I was doing snooping, and prepared to reply that I thought we might have burglars. I called his name twice, but there was no answer. I entered the small room.

It was at the front of the house and I now understood why Mrs Oakes had called it a 'box room': it was much smaller than mine and square like a box. It smelled stale, as if fresh air had never been welcomed in there. The walls were emulsioned in a light blue, and there was a blue-and-cream paisley eiderdown on the bed. The curtains, which I had seen only from outside as I approached the house through the front gate, I now saw to be dark blue with a pattern of black and cream slashes. A single wardrobe and a chest of drawers stood opposite the bed, the space between the furniture and bed no more than three feet and covered by a narrow strip of dark-blue carpet. On the wall by the side of the bed hung what looked like two tortoises and above the head of the bed, next to the drawn curtains, hung another curtain.

With great daring, I switched on the light. My stomach did a somersault as the tortoises became two German helmets, and the 'curtain' above the bed was revealed as a Nazi flag with a huge swastika. German medals and two framed yellowed letters in German sat on top of the chest of drawers, and photographs of Adolf Hitler and other members of the Third Reich adorned the wall above them. I turned to flee – and screamed: hanging on the back of the door was a grey Nazi uniform, the SS insignia on the epaulettes. It looked as if an SS officer had been suspended on Gordon's door, and I thought that if I stayed a second longer, he would materialize. I flicked off the light-switch and ran across the landing and downstairs, and screamed for the second time as I saw a figure standing inside the front door.

'Whatever's wrong, dear?' It was Iris.

'I'm sorry. I've got a bad headache and I went to get my books and I lay down,' I lied. 'I must be late for school and, oh, I still haven't got my books.' Once again I ran upstairs to collect the books I'd intended to get before I'd been drawn into Gordon's strange and frightening room.

'Sure you should go in? You look dead peaky to me, luv. Have an Aspro and a cup of coffee. I shouldn't go in if I was you.'

'No, I've got exams. I've got to go, thanks anyway.'

I ran until I was out of breath. I wasn't late and slowed down when I came in sight of the school. Rosie had been proved right again. It was small comfort that I hadn't seen any guns or knives. Perhaps Gordon kept them in one of the drawers or in the wardrobe. I'd lied to Iris about the exams and about the headache, and now God was paying me back: my head began to ache. It got steadily worse that afternoon and I had a nose-bleed. The school nurse let me lie down in the sick bay, and gave me an aspirin and a cup of tea, which made me feel important. She asked if I wanted to go home, but I told her there would be no one there until five o' clock. Pauline came as the bell went and I wondered if I should tell her what I'd found in Gordon's bedroom, but decided against it.

I was grilling some lamb chops, and potatoes and sprouts were boiling on the stove. Blimp was outside slowly eating his dinner. 'Come on boy, eat up!' I called. He gave me a look of disgust and pushed at his bowl with his nose as if to say, 'I'll take my time.'

'You been in my room today?' Gordon stood behind me, his tone one more of accusation than inquiry.

'No, of course not. Iris was here all dinner hour. I didn't even go upstairs, you can ask her,' I lied indignantly, praying that he wouldn't ask her.

'Oh, OK. The old man's late; d'you want a coffee?'

Amazed at this offer of hospitality from Gordon, I said I'd love one.

'How's school going?' he asked, handing me the coffee. This was truly amazing.

'Fine,' I replied.

'I'll lay the table,' he said. Even more amazing!

I heard Mr Oakes's key in the door and, as dinner was ready to serve, made a mental note that in half an hour another awkward meal would be over. Gordon was decidedly chatty at the dinner table and, since it was St Valentine's Day, I wondered whether he'd received a card from his ex-fiancée. This could have accounted for his laxity in not locking his bedroom door.

After dinner Mr Oakes said he had to see the doctor at the hospital about his wife's pending discharge and aftercare. 'I'm late enough as it is. Drop the gurl over for the last half hour of visiting, son, there's a good lad.'

'Sure.'

It was the first time I'd ever been in Izzie-Bon, and it felt as strange to be getting into the little Issetta, which opened outwards at the front and reminded me of a helicopter, as it did to be to be going anywhere with Gordon. In the cramped confines of the car I thought about his room, and once more my heart began racing. He didn't speak once on the journey to the hospital, which gave me a comforting feeling, as if things were back to normal.

'Aah, now isn't that a nice surprise, to see you two together? Are these for me?'

Gordon had handed his mother a brown paper bag with some apples and a small box of Black Magic chocolates.

'From both of us, Ma,' he muttered as he pulled up chairs for himself and me.

'Been lookin' after you then, has she?' Mrs Oakes looked from one to the other of 'her men'. Her husband agreed that I had, and Gordon said this evening's chops had been a bit 'crunchy', but he'd live.

'I s'pose I could always take her for a spin in Izzie to get my own back.' He pressed the side of his face and opened and closed his mouth, feigning what I took to be toothache. His mother laughed and I nervously joined in.

'You'd like that, ducks, eh? A nice ride in Izzie for half an hour?' I was blushing, unsure whether this was meant to be a serious proposition, until she continued, 'Drive careful now, Gordon. You'll enjoy the break, ducks.' Mrs Oakes patted my hand and Gordon stood up. His mother's face was beaming as I bent to kiss her goodbye.

Mr Oakes didn't seem quite so enthusiastic and told Gordon to be back by half-past eight.

'Oh, it's half-past seven now, Artie. Nine o'clock won't hurt by the time –'

'OK, nine, but no later. If she'd got school tomorrow, it would be half-past eight though.' He pushed his glasses up and down his nose as a mark of disapproval, while Mrs Oakes waved and called out for us to enjoy ourselves.

It was very cold as the little car chugged through the

wintry lanes. Gordon was telling me that you needed only a motor-cycle licence to drive Izzie.

'He can certainly go though!' Gordon accelerated to prove the point and I had visions of the front lid of the car opening and spilling us both out on to the unlit lane like a jar of strawberry jam.

'See, he can go, can't he, eh?'

'Yes, he can,' I agreed, terrified. 'Why does Rosie call you Go-Go? Is it because –?'

'Oh, that stupid bit–' he was going to say 'bitch', but checked himself. My question had distracted him from his driving and he slowed the car down. 'It's my initials, isn't it?'

'Oh! Gordon Oakes. Of course!' I turned my head and smiled at him, but it was dark in the car and he kept his eyes on the road ahead.

'She's stupid, she really is. You don't like her, do you?'

'I didn't, not when she was here for Christmas, but after she left, well, I sort of missed her a bit.'

He didn't speak until a flapping of large whitish feathers flew in front of us, making me jump.

'Did you see that? That was a tawny owl. I love it when you see something like that, it sort of makes evening. If you're lucky we may see a fox.'

'Really?' I asked, silently praying that we wouldn't. For me, owls, foxes and other such creatures belonged in my Alison Utley books, and weren't meant to be seen from a small red earth-bound helicopter

'Fancy a Coca-Cola? There's a little café that stays open?'

'What time is it?'

'Twenty-five to. Don't worry, we'll make it back for

nine.' I agreed, glad to be out of the darkness and inside the café, even though it was poorly lit and smelled of greasy food. I sat on a stool next to Gordon and he bought us each a Coca-Cola and a packet of crisps. I drank half my Coke and decided to open the crisps when I got home, my eyes on a yellow-and-black grease-laden clock. He opened his crisps and offered me one, which I refused.

'So, you like her then?'

I thought he was talking about the car, and told him she went much faster than I thought a car that small could. He spluttered on his drink and looked at me for the first time.

'Not Izzie. Rosie. You like Rosie?'

I repeated my earlier feelings about her, unsure whether I should display disloyalty to any member of his family.

'You don't, do you?'

I felt uncomfortable and looked at him. For the second time since I'd known him he gave me one of his dazzling smiles.

'No, not really.' I returned to my bottle of Coke and finished it, leaving an inch in the bottom in case the air bubbles made a rude noise and embarrassed me.

'Do you like me?'

'You? Well, yes, of course I do!' I wasn't sure that I liked him at all, not after everything Rosie had told me and what I'd seen for myself in his bedroom.

'Do you like me then?' He must do, or he wouldn't have taken me for a drive and bought me Coca-Cola and crisps. I looked at the clock, which showed five minutes to nine, and waited for him to affirm that he did.

'No!'

My blood ran cold. Until now I wouldn't have doubted for one minute that that would have been his answer, but I had been deceived by his apparent kindness this evening. I felt very near to tears, but with great courage, as I watched the clock pass nine, I asked him why he didn't like me.

'Because I don't.'

I felt tears stinging my eyes as I slipped off the stool. I wanted to tell him that I knew all about his Hitler room and his coins and Antoinette or whatever her name was. I wanted to tell him how clearly I could see why she'd left him in the lurch, but instead I just said that I wanted to go as we were late. He drove back to the house in silence, and I went to bed and cried myself to sleep.

Mrs Oakes came home the following day instead of Sunday. I was pleased to have her home, and for the following week I continued to come back from school at midday to make her lunch and feed Blimp. During dinner on Wednesday Mrs Oakes suggested that Gordon take me for another ride in Izzie that evening, but I pleaded too much homework. Gordon himself asked me on Friday night, and this time I claimed a headache – and too much homework. He didn't ask me again; in fact, he stopped speaking to me altogether. Another strange interlude with the Oakeses had taken place and I was back to the *status quo*.

One evening in early March Mr Oakes had taken his wife on one of her convalescent walks with Blimp and I was in my room doing homework when a strange tapping distracted me. I went on to the landing to listen, and realized it was coming from Gordon's room. He was probably putting another picture of his hero, Adolf Hitler, on his bedroom wall.

I still don't know why I did it or from where I summoned the courage, but I walked up to his door and waited until the tapping within stopped. I knocked once and took a step back. The door sprang open and Gordon stood there looking at me.

'My dad had a Luger, you know, a German Luger. It was rusty a bit though, and it had sort of springs you . . .' I was stammering.

'Do you want to come in?'

I stood there mute.

'I know you've been in here.' He spoke softly.

'No, no, I haven't, honestly. Rosie told me you collected Hitler stuff, honest.'

'She would.' His voice was low now.

I started to return to my room and he caught hold of my sleeve.

'No, don't go away, come in.'

'No, I'd better be going. Anyway, you don't like me, you said.'

'No, I don't like you, that's true.' The hand he'd placed on my sleeve was now around my shoulder and he led me gently into the stuffy room. 'Sit down a minute.' He straightened the eiderdown on his unmade bed and patted it for me to sit down.

I did so obediently and he sat beside me.

'I don't like you, I love you,' he said softly, taking one of my hands in his.

I looked at his profile, his head bent, his hand soft in mine. The electric light shone through his thin grey hair, his scalp clearly defined by the light.

'You love me?' I asked in an incredulous whisper.

He turned his head to face me, blue eyes staring into mine. 'Hey, come on. Listen, it's true, I do.'

I remember a tumultuous mixture of emotions: elation, awe, fear. Gordon loved me, and his smile was so gentle. He released my hand and I thought he was going to say it was all a joke. As I turned to get up, he put both arms around me and kissed me gently on the mouth. It was true, he did love me: he'd kissed me.

Suddenly he shoved me gently on to the bed, his hands, like his father's, pushing under my jumper, his mouth pressed hard on mine. I remember thinking that his father had never kissed me in the film-star way, the way Gordon was kissing me now, and I couldn't breathe properly. He seemed to have pinioned me against the bed with his mouth, which was rotating around my pursed lips. I tried to get up but one strong arm held me, a butterfly on a pin, while the other hand tore at his waistband. Again I tried to lift myself. His free hand was now under my skirt, pulling at my navy-blue knickers, down, down past my knees till they were resting on my shins.

What happened next made me cease my struggle. He was splitting me open! My vagina and bottom felt as though he had struck me with an axe, an axe between my legs . . . heat, pain . . . I was a sapling; the axe had split the wood wide open – two, three, four . . . seven, eight times he drove the axe into me until I was split asunder. A scream, primitive and horrifying, was coming from this axe-man and I was whimpering – except that in reality it was Gordon who was whimpering while the screams were coming from my throat. My throat was on fire, and the fire burned between my legs, its flames seared, scorching, the fire of hell.

'I'm sorry, oh, my Christ, what have I done, what have I done?'

I could hear Gordon repeating this over and over. Raising myself up on my elbows, I saw a flash of white underclothes and, as I pulled my knickers up my thighs, I caught sight of his enormous red penis. Sobs tore at my throat at the sight of this new terror. Bent nearly double, I left Gordon's room.

Something warm and sticky was running down my legs from the rent between them and I walked, still bent double, into the bathroom and closed the door. I tried to sit on the edge of the bath, but so violent was my trembling that I nearly fell in. I slid down on to the bathroom floor and waited until the trembling subsided. Drunkenly, I stood up, took the roll of cotton wool from the bathroom cabinet and pulled off a fistful of the white cotton. I ran it under the cold tap and, gritting my teeth, prepared to wipe away the molten lather of blood that I felt running down my legs. As my eyes stole down towards the carnage I had prepared myself for, I shuddered: there was no blood, only a white substance, as if boiling milk was issuing from me. The girls at school had said that when you lost your virginity you lost blood too, but the biology mistress had skimmed over these facts, and I wondered whether the blood would come later and if I'd need a blood transfusion when it did.

The compress did little to help put out the fire, and I sat on the cold enamel of the bath, which gave me some relief. I pulled off my knickers and saw that the elastic had broken on one leg. I remained sitting on the edge of the bath, my arms resting on the sink and my throat aching with my sobs.

I jumped at a noise outside the bathroom door. Someone was running downstairs two at a time. I heard the front door slam, then the sound of an engine starting. Gordon had gone. Swiftly turning the key in the bathroom lock, I ran into my bedroom, grabbed clean underwear and socks, took the dress I'd been given at Christmas out of the wardrobe, and locked myself back in the bathroom.

I poured some Dettol into the cold bath-water and scrubbed myself all over. My skin felt tight from the cold water and soap. I dusted my body with talc, drenched my underarms with deodorant, put on a sanitary towel to await the haemorrhage that would surely come and dressed. Sobs still hiccupped from my throat as I folded the towels and put the clothes I had been wearing into the dirty-linen basket. I muttered, 'There, Gordon, I really am your Drury Lane Whore now.'

I got my coat from my wardrobe and limped downstairs. I dropped the neat newspaper parcel I'd made of my navy-blue knickers into the dustbin as I made my way down the garden path and headed for Pauline's house. It was nearly dark as I shuffled along past the bowling green and towards the area where the lowly market people lived.

13

A car stopped, and I limped along faster. I was sure it was him. A woman's voice called my name twice. I turned and saw that it was his mother.

'Hey, where you off to, dressed up in your best clothes an' all, ducks, eh?'

'Pauline's,' I answered defiantly.

'Get back in the car, Kath. You're still not fully recovered. Let me deal with this.' Mr Oakes had got out of the car and was coming towards me. 'Listen, gurl, it's gone eight. You get in the back seat this minute. Where d'you think you're going? Off with that Pauline to meet some boys, I suppose. Come on, get in the back, it's too cold for Mums to be out. She's only just come out of hospital, remember?' For the second time that evening my sleeve was pulled. He opened the rear door and I gave an involuntary cry as I sat down with a bump on the cold leather.

Inside the car Mr Oakes turned to me before starting the engine. 'Don't think we're gonna stand for you going off with boys with that Pauline at this time of night. Now then, you're not thirteen yet, and it's time you had some thought for others.'

'I want my mummy, I want my mummy, I want her, I want her –'

'Oh God, come on, luvvy. You've not been like this for ages, what's brought this on, eh?'

'I . . . I . . . wasn't going to see any boys. I just wanted to see Pauline and I want my mummy.'

'C'mon now, ducks, calm yourself down. I 'spect you're run down. You been doing a lot of running around since I've been in hospital and recouping? Have a glass of that Sanatogen you bought me for Christmas when we get in, eh? If that don't do the trick, I'll get Dr Andrews out.'

Inside the house I stood in the kitchen as she poured me a glass of her tonic wine.

'Look at your face, all puffy an' all, an' what's happened to your mouth? 'Ere, Artie, look at her mouth. D'you reckon she's caught that infantigo? If she 'as, I'll be up that school, make no mistake. Infantigo comes from dirty homes, like head lice!'

'You don't get dressed up like she is if you're feeling ill. Boys it is, Kath.'

'Now listen, Artie, she's not interested in boys. I know her, see, and I'll thank you not to say it again. Come on, luvvy, it's bed for you, you're run down or you're coming down with something.'

An axe is what I've come down with Mrs Oakes, it has split me in two, but this tonic wine will seal the rent in my body and it shall be whole again, a little charring maybe, Mrs Oakes, a little charring, nothing more.

'Where's our Gordon, Artie? He didn't mention he was going out tonight, did he? Izzie's not outside. Did he say he might be going out?'

'I think he was going over to Gerry's, but I can't remember whether it was today or Thursday. Must have been today, Kath. What time did he go out?' Mr Oakes directed his question to me and I shrugged my shoulders and shook my head. I could feel the tears springing to the surface and swallowed hard. Perhaps he'd had a car crash, perhaps he'd gone too fast around those country lanes and hit a fox. I hoped the fox was all right and Gordon was dead, tipped out of his red bubble car, the top of the jar open and the contents spilled across the road, strawberry jam that once was Gordon Oakes.

As I climbed into bed, having scrubbed myself again and ensured that the dampness between my legs was not the start of the expected blood loss, I knew that tonight would be my very last in this bed. Tomorrow I was running away and no one was going to stop me. I'd go to Auntie Ada and Rosie. Rosie would believe me. It was Rosie who'd been telling the truth. I was just another hobby, something Mr Oakes had played with for a while and then discarded, like the puppies, canaries and kittens; my cage had been larger than theirs, that was all. Gordon had made me his hobby now, but I was going to discard him, like the girl with the French name had, and Rosie would believe me, of that I was certain.

I awoke in the night. The axe that had bitten into the tender young bark had left its sap aflame. I crept quietly into the bathroom and made another compress of cotton wool. The icy water stung and cooled. I searched the cabinet for the witch-hazel and instead found a bottle of pink calamine lotion. I applied it liberally to my injuries and experienced some relief. I swallowed two aspirin with water from the tooth mug.

I turned on the bedside lamp and looked at the clock. It was 4.15. The lamp by the bed gave me an idea. Mrs Oakes was always saying that too strong a light could lead to blindness, and I'd heard somewhere that staring into an electric light bulb for ten minutes would produce this result. Now I stared into the bulb of my bedside lamp until black and bright spots appeared before my eyes and they began to stream. Still I persevered, waiting for the black spots to merge into a final blackness that would blot out the light of the world for ever and leave me in the darkness I now craved. People would feel sorry for me if I were blind, I would have a white stick and no one would hurt me ever again. My eyelids felt bruised and heavy by the time I switched off the lamp. Flashes of light lit my darkness and I knew that in the morning that I would no longer see.

I heard the telephone ring and Mrs Oakes open my bedroom door and close it again. I heard them both go to the bathroom and their bedroom door shut.

I awoke with my eyes very sore, but my vision perfect. Although it was still very early, the mornings were growing lighter now, and I wished for the darkness of the winter mornings to return to envelop and comfort me. My vagina and bottom felt terribly sore, tight and bruised, and I recoiled with horror from the fact that my virginity, unlike my eyesight, was no longer intact.

I got out of bed unsteadily and a shower of pink dust fell from my pyjama bottoms. In my confusion I wondered if this was another symptom of the loss of virginity until I realized it was the dried calamine lotion!

Gently, I pulled off my pyjama top and examined my breasts. There were no marks. I put on my dressing-gown and walked gingerly into the bathroom. As I took off my pyjama trousers, another cloud of pink dust fell to the floor. I knew from the aching in my sides and inner thighs, along with the burning pain inside me, that I was very badly bruised. I didn't want to look; it would only make me full of self-pity and then I'd cry again. I unravelled the last of the cotton wool, filled the basin with cold water and sponged myself again and again. The water turned an innocent pinky hue as I washed off the calamine lotion, and finally remained clear after it was changed for the third time. I sat on the edge of the bath and gently patted my lower torso dry with a towel, not daring to look down.

Once dry, I shuddered and forced myself to look at my injuries. I couldn't believe it – there was nothing! No angry tear marks, no red, mauve and blue bruises – nothing! Only the pain persisted, reminding me of the reality of what had happened in the Hitler room should I wish to deny it in my mind. On further scrutiny by the light of the bathroom window I found two small cigar-shaped bruises, a faint mauve-and-brown one inside my upper left thigh and a million pinpricks of blood tinged with blue, as if the skin was chapped, on my upper legs. There seemed to be a blurred outline around my mouth and slight bruising to my lower lip. I was shocked at the paucity of evidence of injury.

I thought I heard a movement within the house. My heart began to beat very fast. I listened and all was silent again. Hugging my dressing-gown tightly to me, I went into the bedroom. I put on another clean vest and, with great pain, pulled on a pair of white knickers trimmed with lace, once again padding myself in case the delayed blood loss occurred. I winced as I put on new white knee-length socks, my Christmas dress and a red cardigan. As I was buttoning the cardigan I wondered if Mrs Oakes would miss me preparing the vegetables this morning. The carrots, onions, parsnips and turnips would be down there in the colander waiting to be topped and tailed.

I'm sorry to leave the vegetables, Mrs Oakes, but you see, I can't stay in a house where your husband 'topped' me and your son 'tailed' me, and I wish I could have stayed, just you and me, Mrs Oakes, just you and me.

Tears spilled down my face, burning my sore lips. I made my bed quickly, then took the kitten box from under the dressing-table. I stuffed the scarf, book and the new envelope with the lock of hair into my satchel, along with my deodorant and talc, a clean pair of knickers, socks and a vest. I emptied my money box and found I had £3. 7s. 6d., which I transferred to my red purse. Putting on my coat and red scarf and mittens, I made my way, satchel bulging, downstairs and out of the front gate, wincing as it closed with a loud snap. I walked swiftly among my early-morning friends, who were heading towards the station for the London train. I felt guilty at letting down Mr Taylor, the newsagent, and wondered at what point he'd telephone the Oakeses. Keeping my scarf muffled up around my mouth, I walked to the town as fast as my aching body would carry me, looking around every hundred yards or so, imagining Mr Oakes or Gordon in Izzie-Bon in hot pursuit.

Reaching the town unrecognized and unassailed, I went to the coach station and waited fretfully for half an hour until it opened. I purchased a ticket to London; I would have to change once and wait forty minutes for the connecting coach. I breathed a sigh of relief as the bus carried me away from the town.

The first sight of an Underground sign made me alight. I hurried into the station and the pleasant pipe-tobacco smell and warmth rushed at me, its familiarity a welcoming embrace. How could I have forgotten the unmistakable smell of the London Tube?

By twelve o'clock, after a succession of wrong changes, I was back at my old home, the red brick of the Mansions strangely forbidding, yet welcoming too. Entering the dark passageway, I knocked on the familiar knocker, surprised at how much easier it was to reach now that a year had passed – or perhaps it had been lowered. My heart was beating a tattoo in time to the pain in my sides. I knocked several times and looked through the letter-box. All the doors must have been closed, for I could see only the darkness of a deserted hallway.

Slowly, I went round the corner and knocked on the doors of three of Mummy's friends. Although one letter-box showed some light in a hallway with a red runner of carpet, the second was dark and the third obscured by a heavy curtain, and all failed to give any indication that the occupants were at home. My imagination ran wild: I wondered if they knew it was me and didn't want to see me again. The orange candle flared and the flame fanned its message to my brain. Perhaps they knew how Mummy had died. The flame grew in intensity and singed my very soul, growing into an inferno that seemed to envelop me. Perhaps I had died and was in purgatory, a ghost stalking my home, a ghost that no one could see!

Defeated, I walked outside slowly and ran my hand along the cold red brick of the Mansions as far as our front-room window, where strange new curtains now hung. No, I wasn't a ghost. A little further along the wall I saw the scar that had been gouged into the brick: 'C.F. loves D.M. true'. As if my wish to be rendered blind the night before had been granted, I traced the indentation into the brick with my ungloved forefinger, and remembered the fight I'd had with my brother James over that. Donald Mason, whom I had once loved, had left the Mansions before my mother had died; a fleeting recollection of his face came and was gone. I turned my head towards the cold rain that had begun to spit at my face.

I could have caught a bus, but decided to walk in the lightly falling rain to the house where my grandmother had rooms. I rang her bell, expecting I would have to wait for her to descend the stairs, but I'd have waited for ever. After about five minutes I nervously pressed the next white button where a relatively new lodger lived. The third button down would spell trouble – it was the landlady's – but I was desperate and the rain was falling heavily now. Still there was no response. I rang each bell again and counted to a hundred. I looked through the letter-box, and the scent of stale food, dust, old furniture and gas from the gas lamps assailed my nostrils. I could see the wooden hall-stand standing to attention as always, a tree whose branches carried all manner of coats smelling of mothballs. Trilby hats, panamas and a bowler adorned its uppermost branches and lower down a ring of wood held umbrellas, walking sticks and feather dusters. Suddenly I heard a noise from the area below. It was 'Blackie Beetle', the strange old man from the basement, who still lived with his black-out curtains up.

'Bugger off, git out, go on or I'll git the bleedin' bobbies, I've gotta whistle ya know . . .'

My voice went unheard amid his shouting, and I beat a hasty retreat, as we had always done from Blackie Beetle. I caught a bus to Auntie Ruth's house, but by the time I got there it was no surprise to me to find that it too was empty.

I began walking aimlessly and came to the bridge to which Mummy used to bring us. It was smaller in reality than it was in my dreams, but I remembered how she would pick us up to watch the trains. A roar from the tunnel below and the sight of the emerging train renewed my sense of loss. A rumble of thunder indicating the approach of another train made me leave the bridge and walk towards the shops. Thoroughly wet by now, I entered the warmth of a Lyons Corner House.

I drank the hot tea and picked at the strands of white coconut on the cheesecake, wondering what to do next. Two men came to my table and I got up to leave. I didn't want company; I had to be alone to think.

'Just a minute, luv.'

A restraining hand on my arm made me sit down again with a thump. I winced from the pain.

'Bit upset, aren't you, luv?'

I shook my head, droplets of water cascading around the table.

'We've been following you.'

My heart was thumping wildly now. Oh God, these must be the School Board men; they'd been sent to find me. As if to confirm my suspicion, the one who had been doing all the talking said, 'Playing truant then, are you? Coo, I can talk! D'you know something? I used to get ten outa ten for that, when I was at school that is. What about you, Pete?'

His friend shook his head. 'No, not me, Ken, I didn't

get any marks. I tell a lie – I did, but only from the cane! What you got there then? Tea, is it? Yes, you can't mistake Joe Lyon's tea. His coffee's OK, though. We were just going to have one. Can I get you one as well?'

'No, this is . . .' I picked up my cup of cold tea, as if to indicate I was enjoying it.

'Something to eat then, eh? You're not enjoying that old cheesecake. You look like a sparrow picking at a worm, and not a very tasty one at that!' Pete laughed and Ken joined in.

'No, thanks, its just that I thought I was hungry but –'

'No sparrow can be that hungry, eh? If you ask me, that came outa the oven with Alfred's burnt ones. Usual?' Pete asked Ken.

Ken nodded and turned his attention to me as his friend went off to get their coffee.

'Where'd you live, luv? You're not local, are you?' he asked.

I shook my head, showering more droplets on the table. Ken, who seemed young, took a white handkerchief out of his pocket and told me to 'wipe my noddle'. I patted my head with the hanky, thanked him and gave it back. Pete returned bearing a tray with three cups of coffee and three jam doughnuts.

'Here, I thought you might be tempted if you saw ours, but if you really don't want them, that's no problem. Ken here is a human dustbin, aren't you, Kenneth?' Once seated, Pete continued, 'We've been following you, my love.'

My body, already cold and wet, seemed to freeze. I looked round the Corner House. It was half full. If they were murderers or something and tried to take me away, I'd scream until the police came. Almost as if they had read my thoughts, both men simultaneously put their hands inside their overcoats and pulled out leather squares inscribed 'M.P.' above photographs that didn't look particularly like either of them.

'These are warrant cards, luvvy. CID.'

I was still holding one of the cards when Pete gently extracted it from my fingers.

'Are you from Scotland Yard?' My eyes had widened and my voice held a tremor.

'No, we're local. Plainclothes. You must have seen blokes like us on the telly. Not as good looking, of course,' he said, laughing.

'Or as poor,' Ken interjected.

'What's your name, luv, eh?'

I didn't answer.

'C'mon, tell us your name. I bet it's a pretty one. Penny? Sally? Annabelle?'

I remained mute.

'Where d'you live, darlin'? We can easily find out, so it'll save us a lot of time and trouble if you tell us. You should be in school, shouldn't you?'

I nodded.

'What were you doing standing on the bridge, eh? Weren't thinking of saying "goodbye cruel world", were you?' Pete asked, his voice soft.

I didn't understand what his last question meant and looked at him quizzically.

'You weren't thinking of jumping off it, the bridge I mean, were you? You wouldn't have got far, me and Ken were right behind you ready –'

'No! I used to come to see the trains with Mummy

when ... sometimes I dream about it – the bridge, I mean. I dream she's under there. I know it's silly.' My voice came in stilted phrases.

'You've come a long way to see a bridge if –'

'My mummy's dead, all my family are gone now, I came back to ...' The whole story came tumbling out, with the exception of the events of last night. 'I just missed them so, so I came back.' My voice trailed off.

Ken, the policeman I'd been sitting next to, placed an arm around me and stroked my damp hair. It was Pete's turn to proffer a hankie and Ken mopped my tears.

'Are you in Dr "Bananas", darlin'?' Pete asked gently.

I shook my head.

'Tell us where then, there's a good girl. We want to help you, honest we do, and you've not done anything wrong. Or have you?'

The sudden change in his voice frightened me and I shook my head hard in fierce denial.

'You won't take me back there?' I asked.

'Not if you don't want us to, but –'

'No, I mean you won't let them know that you know what I've done?'

'Tell us about "them", darlin'. Who are they?' Ken said, releasing his arm from around my shoulder. 'Is it a big home you're in, lots of other kids, some bullies, eh?'

'No, it's a foster-home.' Reluctantly, I gave them my name and address.

'Ah, so there's your foster-mum and dad, and just the one boy. Is he fostered too?'

'No, he's theirs.'

'Whew! Well, you've certainly got a posh address and look at your posh clothes and all. What does your foster-dad do then, eh?' Pete asked.

He used to 'top' me and now Gordon's 'tailed' me, officer.

'He works for the Government, I think.'

'Look, darlin', it must be hard for you, but you could be a lot worse off, you know. What if you were in one of those big homes? You'd just be a number in one of them. They've got what I believe are called House-mothers and Housefathers and rules and regulations. Aren't I right, Ken?'

Yes, I know. I've been there too, officer, but no one 'topped' or 'tailed' me there, and there were others the same as me there, officer!

'If we take you back, these people are going to be so relieved. They're obviously gonna be upset, but they're intelligent people from the sound of things; they'll under-stand you wanted to come back home. After all, you wouldn't be normal if you didn't miss –'

'Please, can I go back on my own?' I interrupted. 'I promise I will. They won't even know I've gone if I leave now.'

'No, I'll tell you what we'll do. We'll go to the station now – we've got a smashin' police lady who'll look after you. Now then, have you got a Welfare Officer you know of?'

I nodded and with great trepidation gave them Miss Crowley's name, even supplying her telephone number, much to their surprise.

'We'll go and let Sue, the police lady, look after you. She loves children, and we'll get on to this Miss . . . er, Crowley.' He looked down to check her name. 'We'll put you on the train and get her to meet you the other end, eh? Then she can let us know you got home safely and weren't beaten over the head with a mallet by your foster-mum and dad when you got there, OK?'

An hour later the two CID men put me on the train as promised, with a packet of Spangles and the *Schoolfriend* comic, but not before they'd given me a card with their names on it and a two-shilling piece.

'Give your little brother a bob out of that,' Ken told me.

My little brother, officer, who split my body in two – a shilling for the axe-man, officer? Yes, officer.

Miss Crowley was not pleased with me. She'd had no word from the Oakeses, but they were kind and considerate people, and I would have to apologize, and didn't I stop to consider how lucky I was to have got such a placement?

An hour later, with Mrs Oakes red-eyed, her husband's pallid and yellow, we were all seated around the dining-table, sipping tea with Miss Crowley. Everyone understood that they could never take the place of my real family, but they were trying. Things had been a bit unsettled of late, yes, what with Mrs Oakes having to go into hospital. And, yes, they had to admit that Rosie, their niece, had been rather unkind to me over Christmas, and it had been my first Christmas away from ... but, ahh well, Rosie wouldn't prove a problem any more, that was the least of their worries; a good talking to by her aunt and uncle would put paid to Rosie's nonsense. If I really wasn't settling, then Miss Crowley could make other arrangements, although she couldn't guarantee I'd have all the comforts and care ... The discomfort and bruising in my lower torso seemed to react to the very word and I shifted gingerly on the hard chair.

Mrs Oakes crushed a lace handkerchief against her mouth as fresh tears welled in her eyes, and her husband jiggled his glasses up and down his nose at a fast pace with his index finger. As I looked up for a brief second, my eyes met his, and I knew, knew beyond all doubt, that he wanted me gone, gone to join his other discarded hobbies. But, as Rosie had pointed out, they hadn't had a human one before. *What to do with a human hobby when the novelty had worn off? Now there's the rub Mr Oakes.*

Mr Taylor, it seemed, had alerted them when I hadn't turned up for my paper round. Mrs Oakes had telephoned the school and Mr Oakes had come home from work. Poor Gordon, who'd stayed the night at his friend Gerry's, had also been summoned from work and was still out looking for me. Another half an hour and they were going to phone Miss Crowley and the police!

A key in the door and footsteps in the hall, hovering, making no move to enter the dining-room, caused his mother to call out, 'Gordon, is that you, luv? In here, we've found her, she's all right. Gordon! Come and sit down. There's tea in the pot.'

Gordon entered the dining-room.

'C'mon, sit down, Gordon, son. Been back to Pauline's house, have you? Teapot needs a bit of a freshner, luvvy. Be a good girl and top it up. Kettle's on the boil. Get Gordon a fresh cup and saucer.'

I left the dining-room with relief. The teapot's lid rattled under my trembling grasp and I placed my free hand on top of it to silence the noise. I put a teaspoon of tea into the pot, filled it with boiling water and quietly took a cup and saucer from the kitchen cabinet. I listened at the door of the kitchen.

'No, the police were very good, they're used to this sort of thing. Unusual for the CID to get involved . . . a bridge . . . asked if she'd ever expressed any desire to do away with herself . . . able to reassure them on that point of course . . . past history gave them a little more insight . . . they were concerned . . . but then at this age . . .'

I began to rattle the cup and saucer. I placed them on a tray, having managed to eavesdrop on most of Miss Crowley's discourse, and re-entered the dining-room. Miss Crowley looked up and gave me a beaming smile.

'Ah, there you are, deah. Your mum here is going to take you to see Dr Andrews. We think you may need a bit of a check-up, just to see that everthing's hunky-dory, as it were. It's best, we think. Aah, yes, I will have another cup and then I must be going.'

Mrs Oakes poured her another cup of tea and handed one to her son, who was leaning against the sideboard. I stared at him. He was puffing furiously on a cigarette. It was the fact that he was smoking that startled me. He was deathly pale and wiping the perspiration from his brow with the hand that held the cigarette awkwardly. There was a faint, brief buzzing sound as the cigarette singed his thin grey hair.

The following day Dr Andrews, having looked at my throat, ears, eyes and listened to my chest, examined my nails, and taken my temperature and pulse, pronounced me fit, going through puberty and in need of a tonic. This came in the form of a huge bottle of green elixir that contained iron, since, he'd explained, I was a little anaemic. This was the panacea prescribed by the good doctor. My aching lower torso was left for Mother Nature to mend.

It was a week before I could ride my bike, so I had to get up an hour earlier to do my paper round on foot. As I returned, with an aching shoulder, on the Saturday morning I saw that the heavy winter curtains were being taken down by Gordon and his father and the summer ones hung in their place. The same stepladder, the same precision, the ritual ending with the winter curtains being folded and put into their Sketchley Cleaners bag. The changing of the curtains had taken place again, and now the event filled me with apprehension – what did spring and the changing seasons hold for me? I shivered as I laid the *Daily Mail* on the dining-table and went into the kitchen to make myself a cup of Nescafé.

14

My thirteenth birthday arrived and only Mrs Oakes seemed oblivious of the atmosphere that surrounded us whenever I had to be with 'her men'. Mr Oakes no longer called me 'gurl' quite so often, and Gordon hovered around as if to say something, but never quite managing to do so, although he would speak politely when he had to. My entry into the teens was accompanied by the greatest gift anyone could have bestowed upon me: two bras, size 32A, for my 'bee-stings', Mrs Oakes said laughingly, embarrassed at my display of affection and gratitude as I threw my arms around her and kissed her. She had also made me a rock 'n' roll skirt, a paper-nylon petticoat and a pretty pink blouse.

Auntie Ada sent me a white cardigan and Rosie a pale pink lipstick and a jar of vanishing cream. 'I'm not giving a hint with the cream, but me Mum and me will be down the second two weeks in July, hope you like the lipstick, name's good "Hot Lips" don't you rekkon?' she had written in her childish scrawl on the card. She had signed off with a heart-shaped pattern of crosses (or kisses) with 'Rosie' written in the middle. It looked like a funeral wreath, but to Rosie it was probably a work of art.

Mr and Mrs Knightley bought me a white clutch handbag, and Pauline gave me a white suspender belt and a pair of nylons. Mr Oakes put his foot down about common underwear and nylons and Rosie's lipstick. Mrs Oakes said that I could put the lipstick on in the bathroom, but to make sure he didn't see me wearing it and to wipe it off again with the vanishing cream Rosie had sent. Gordon had put a pound note in his card, which just read 'from Gordon'.

Pauline came to tea on my birthday. Mrs Oakes had made a sponge cake and a trifle. She decorated the top of the sponge with white icing and hundreds and thousands, and put a candle in the middle. Ham and tomato sandwiches and bridge rolls with pink salmon and cress adorned the table, and I was really excited. Mr Oakes wasn't very amiable even though I'd tried to chat to him more than I'd ever done before. I had seen Pauline chatter away to her Dad in this fashion, and their conversation had always been punctuated with laughter. Mine fell on stony ground. Gordon's attempts to be witty were also unsuccessful, although he was more animated than usual. Mrs Oakes was nice to Pauline, but I knew she was looking disapprovingly at Pauline's peach-coloured lipstick, nylon stockings and 'Louis-heeled' shoes. It was when Pauline pushed back her hair with hairslides and revealed gold bands piercing her soft pink ear lobes that I knew her fate had been sealed: Pauline was unsuitable. By the time they'd sung a patchy 'Happy Birthday' and I'd blown out the candle, Pauline was looking at the clock. Mrs Oakes said I could walk home with Pauline, but was to be back in an hour.

As we walked past the bowling green Pauline said she didn't blame me for trying to see my Gran, which was the excuse I'd given her for my day off school and Gordon's inquiries at her house as to my whereabouts.

Pauline's verdict was that the Oakeses were a stuck-up bunch of old fogeys, but the house was nice and my bedroom was better than hers and Deirdre's.

I'd toyed with the idea of confiding in Pauline about the real reason for my running away, and had even rehearsed my lines. But then I thought she wouldn't believe that old fogeys like Mr Oakes and Gordon could do things like that, and she might tell Deirdre and she wouldn't believe me either. If I lost Pauline and Deirdre's trust I'd have lost everything. I could hear Deirdre saying, 'Now let's get this straight. You knocked at his door and then he did that. What were you doing knocking on his door? What did you go there for?' What indeed, Deirdre, what indeed? I knew I was to blame for knocking on that door and the flame that was my conscience flared and singed my soul.

I still lay awake at night waiting for Gordon and Mr Oakes to pay their final visit to the bathroom and for each door to shut.

Daffodils, tulips and other spring flowers heralded the new season, and the mornings were light as I did my paper round. I carried the memories of my mother and my family with me as I disposed of the morning's newspapers. Sometimes the lighter the bag grew, the heavier my heart became. I remembered the daffodils wrapped in newspaper on Mother's Day, and Mummy's delight at the handmade cards we would proudly present to her.

There would be no handmade card for Mrs Oakes, but one bought from Mr Taylor's shop, and her garden held armfuls of daffodils. I sought advice, and Mr Oakes recommended a scarf and some hand lotion. I couldn't remember Mummy ever using any creams, only her

Evening in Paris perfume. If she came back now I would buy her scarves and creams and blue bottles of Evening in Paris and nylon stockings and armfuls of spring flowers. I thought about the cars full of roses there'd been when she'd died, red roses the colour of flames, and again the candle ignited and the part in her death that Daddy said I had played seared at my soul, and no tears, no spring showers could quench that flame.

The flame had a new dimension now, as it could scorch me with a reminder that I'd wanted Mr Oakes's love, and he'd 'topped' me and stopped loving me after I'd broken his glasses. Then I'd begun to look to Gordon, my heart happily skipping a beat as he'd stood up for me against his father's and Rosie's unkindness, only to feel leaden in my chest when he said that he didn't like me. How I'd cried myself to sleep over that! Elation had swept through me when he said he loved me, but afterwards he had torn me apart. I wanted to put everything back the way it had been, but my London Bridge had burned down and all I had left was fire, and no water to pour on the flames.

My chance to rebuild the bridge came in July, the occasion of Mr Oakes's birthday. At various times he'd talked to Mrs Oakes about getting a myna bird and now the chance of buying one came along. A friend of Pauline's parents who kept a pet shop on the market said I could have one and he'd knock ten shillings off the price for me. I raced home from school to impart the good news to Mrs Oakes.

'Ooh, luvvy, he'll love that, but you can't afford to spend all that on your own. Now listen. Gordon and me will chip in, and he won't know no different, and we could buy him the cage and all the bits and bobs he'll need. Ooh, I'm excited myself! Is he young, d'you know? Well, this time of the year he should be. We used to breed canaries, did you know?'

'No, I didn't know,' I lied. The memory of Rosie's talk flickered briefly in my mind, but I ignored it; this was a happy day.

'So you can tell your friend in the pet shop that we're experienced with birds, he'll have a good home. I'll go and phone our Gordon. Are you sure you've got enough to put down that deposit?'

I assured her I had, and raced upstairs to get the two pounds out of my money box.

Gordon arranged to pick up the myna, as well as a cage and food and all the other requirements, so that the present would be complete when Mr Oakes came in on the night of his birthday. The bird was to be put in the unused lounge, to which Mr Oakes would be escorted after dinner.

That night after we'd eaten a dinner of ham salad, Mrs Oakes brought in the sponge cake she had made for her husband; it was identical to the one she'd made for me, down to the one candle. He unwrapped the shirt she had bought him and said 'Very nice darling, umm', and kissed her cheek. Gordon gave his father a tie to go with the shirt and a package he said wasn't to be opened until after they'd had their coffee. Mr Oakes looked a little baffled, examined the package more closely and asked if it was one of Gordon's daft games.

'Come on, Artie. Come and see what lies behind the mystery parcel.'

'Wait a bit, Kath. I haven't finished my coffee,' he protested.

'I'll make you another one, come on.' Mrs Oakes, her

face flushed with excitement, persuaded her husband to his feet. 'C'mon, Artie, hurry up, and you two!'

We all trooped into the lounge, and Mrs Oakes went straight to the window and drew back the curtains. The evening sun momentarily hurt our eyes and threw a reddish hue on the myna bird's large steel cage, which was suspended on an equally gleaming steel stand. The myna bird immediately gave a squawk, which sounded more like a groan, as if it had a sore throat.

'Oh, Kath, oh darling, look at that, look, just look!' He was kissing his wife, his face alight, his glasses slipping down his nose. He pushed them firmly back on to the bridge of his nose with his index finger.

'Hey, Artie, it's not from me nor our Gordon; it's from this young lady here!'

'Really?' He looked at his wife and then at his son, who confirmed that the bird was indeed my present, without even mentioning that they'd subsidized the purchase.

'We bought you the cage and stand, me and our Gordon. No, the little lady here, she just supplied the bird.'

'Oh boy! Thank you, sweetheart.' He kissed my cheek and held me to him for the briefest of moments. Once again he kissed his wife and shook Gordon's hand. 'Thanks, son, thanks. It's bloomin' marvellous.'

He opened the complicated door at the front of the cage, put his hand inside and stroked the top of the black bird's head very gently.

'You're not very old, are you, sweetie, eh?' He made squeaky sounds to the bird, pushing his lips in and out, and stroked the myna's bright yellow beak, which prompted the bird to make its groaning noise again. I thought the bird would try to peck him and took a step backwards. Mr Oakes continued to make soothing noises to the bird and began to whistle.

'Now then, are you a lady or a gent, eh?' he cooed.

'They said it was a girl in the shop,' I offered.

'Artie! P'raps we could breed from her, eh, what do you think?'

'First things first, Kath. I'm gonna get this little one talkin' not squawkin' before we start thinking of you raising a family, aren't I, eh? We haven't even a name for you yet, little one, have we now? That's important, isn't it?' Once again the bird gave its squawky groan. 'You'd better learn how to talk properly, not groan and moan. Hey, I've got it! I've got her name – it's Mona, Mona the Myna!' Everyone laughed, and Mr Oakes spent some time fussing with the cage and water and cuttlefish and birdseed and stuff that I didn't know birds ate or drank.

Mrs Oakes and I left the lounge to wash up, but Gordon and his father stayed there with Mona for at least an hour.

'Well, ducks, I can honestly say you made a clever choice when you heard about that bird. It's years since he's been so delighted with anything.'

When they returned to the dining-room, Gordon pointed to the package on the table. It was, of course, a book on myna birds, their origins, habits, care in captivity and how to gain their confidence in talking and the extent of their vocabulary. Mr Oakes read the vital information this book contained out loud to us.

'Eh, the swear-words are in the back, Dad,' Gordon said, and his father flicked through the back of the book. Realizing his son was joking, he made a pretext

164

of cuffing him around the head with the book, which had us all laughing.

That night I was given a glass of wine with them, and I felt as if I'd put a piece of my broken life back together again. Mr and Mrs Oakes were both a little tipsy. She called me 'darling' when she said goodnight, and he called me 'sweetheart'.

I went to bed happier than I'd been for a long time. Even Gordon had given me an affectionate brotherly grin as he said goodnight. I smiled back and thanked him for helping me to buy the myna. He waved a hand as if to say 'forget it'.

15

The wine and the lateness of the night made me fall
asleep almost at once. I was dreaming that the myna
bird was travelling with me and Gordon in Izzie. It had
been sitting on my lap and suddenly its black feathers
changed to white and fluttered in my face. I pushed
away at the white feathers and awoke with a start,
rubbing my hand across my face. My hand brushed
against the warmth of another human hand. I turned
my body towards the wall, feigning sleep, and kept very
still, trying to keep my breathing even. The familiar
throb of fear started in my spine and I lay very still,
daring only to cross my fingers and pray, oh how I
prayed, that whoever it was, Gordon or his father,
would go away. I felt pressure on the side of the bed
and warm breath approaching my cheek. The mattress
sank further and the quickened breathing was close to
my hair. Suddenly a finger traced over my brows, my
eyes, my nose and down to my throat. The night was
hot and I was wearing a thin cotton nightie. The fingers
continued to trace their route over my left breast, kneading and pinching the soft flesh. Lips touched my cheek.
I could smell wine. Oh God, which one was it? It had to
be Gordon – I shouldn't have smiled; he'd taken it as a
sign of forgiveness. Oh God, why did I ask for this to
happen to me?

'Oh, you want me, don't you, you want it,' the voice whispered.

A hand reached under my shoulder, which was now lying flat against the mattress, and pulled me over on to my back. I grunted, as if the intrusion into my sleep had been momentary, and lay there on my back, my eyes still tightly closed. Both my breasts were now free to be mauled, the nipples pinched and plucked.

'Ooh, sweetheart, sweetheart.' Mr Oakes's breath was coming in shorter, sharper gasps.

I threw myself on to my stomach with sudden violence and strength, strength I never knew I possessed. 'Oh no, no, no!' I screamed, as his hand was momentarily twisted beneath me. I heard him stumble to his feet and steady himself against the wardrobe. Then the door opened, and I thought he was leaving.

'What the hell?' It was Gordon.

'I think she's having a nightmare or some –'

'What's happened, Artie?' came Mrs Oakes's voice.

'Caroline's having a nightmare, Ma, you'd better go in to her,' Gordon advised his mother.

I heard the click as my bedside lamp was switched on, and the chinking of Mrs Oakes's curlers.

'You all right, luvvy, eh?'

I still lay on my stomach, and the sobs held at bay for so long came out in one long ugly howl. 'Someone was in the room, Mm, someone was in the room and he . . . he . . . he tried to . . .'

'Shush, shush now, you've had a bad dream, that's all. Must have been the wine, doesn't agree with you. There now, luvvy, there. Mums'll go and make you some hot milk and nutmeg, best thing for bad dreams.'

I was clutching at her hand and pleading with her not

to leave me, but she eventually released my hand and, curlers tinkling, left the room for what seemed half an hour or more, but could only have been minutes. She returned with a mug of warm milk with the brown spice floating on the top. After I'd finished the milky drink, she stayed stroking my hair, which was as wet as it had been the day in Lyons Corner House with the two policemen. I tried to remember where I'd put their card; I knew I'd hidden it. Mrs Oakes got up and placed a cool, damp flannel on my head and face. My hair stuck to the pillow with perspiration, a dry white handkerchief mopping at my rain-drenched hair, the policeman called Ken . . .

'I'll leave my door open and yours, luvvy. Nothing can harm you. Leave your lamp on, eh? There, you're safe now, go to bye-byes.' Quietly she left the room.

But the spider can come into my parlour, Mrs Oakes. I am the fly and your spider has left me on my back helpless while he spins his web to entrap me once more. Close your door, Mrs Oakes. Don't let him spin his web, a web I may not be able to untangle myself from next time, Mrs Oakes.

I lay awake until dawn. If only I hadn't bought that bird . . . Of the many terrors I have known in my life, that night is one of the worst, and the memory of it still makes my pulse race and my fingers tremble.

I was late for my paper round in the morning and everything seemed to go wrong in my world, a world that last night had seemed hopeful. I made three mistakes in my deliveries and as I knocked on a door to exchange a wrongly delivered paper, giving only a muffled apology, a thrush flew across my path. I stood shaking as I watched it in its uncertain flight. I would fear birds for the rest of my life.

Mr Oakes was sitting waiting for his newspaper when I came into the dining-room bearing the *Daily Mail* and a cup of coffee, which Mrs Oakes had handed to me on my way through the kitchen. Gordon was sitting at the table with his father.

'Thanks. Late this morning, luv?' Mr Oakes asked as he picked up the newspaper.

'Yes, I was.'

'Better now? Bad dream, was it?' Gordon mumbled.

'No!'

'Well, let's know when you do have one then; you were pretty scared.'

'I didn't have a bad dream.' I wasn't sure where this determination was coming from.

'Eh, well, nightmare then, I s'pose you'd call it,' Gordon persisted.

'No! It wasn't a nightmare either.'

Mr Oakes was noisily turning the pages of the paper as if to drown out our exchange.

'Cheese!' Mrs Oakes tinkled her way into the room, a toast rack in one hand. 'Cheese!' she repeated, putting the toast rack down and looking pleased with herself. 'Cheese and ham salad for dinner last night. Cheese causes bad dreams. That's what did for you, ducks. No more cheese at night from now on, d'you hear me? Now tuck in or you'll be late.'

Pleased with her diagnosis of the cause of the night's disturbance, Mrs Oakes poured herself and the bespectacled object she had married another cup of tea. Mr Oakes, the 'cheese' of my nightmare, wrapped himself in the newspaper with much crackling.

'You should have seen Dads with Mona this morning,' Mrs Oakes was announcing proudly.

You should have seen Dads with me last night, I thought bitterly and, excusing myself from the table, ran upstairs to change into my uniform and examine the previous night's injuries. There was no bruising on either breast as yet, just the familiar flecks of blood around one nipple. I decided I would have to wear a bra for protection night and day.

Mr Oakes was waiting outside the bathroom door. 'OK now, sweetheart?'

A warm rage, suppressed so often over the past sixteen months, broke through what was 'allowed' behaviour. I could feel my teeth clench and I heard my own voice as if from a long way off, the words spewing out as a growl.

'What do you mean, OK? OK after my bad dream, nightmare, too much cheese or you again? No, I'm not OK. I'm not, and I've got marks to prove it, you filthy old bastard.' My heart was racing so fast now that I knew it must surely stop, and he would breathe a sigh of relief. 'She died, her heart stopped beating, officer,' I could hear him saying, his head bent in mourning.

'Prove what?' The calmness of his voice stopped me and only the way he was sliding his glasses up and down his nose gave any indication of agitation. 'I repeat, prove what, luvvy?' He stood perfectly composed, almost tranquil, his face a picture of both consternation and concern.

This totally confused me. He looked so, so ... *innocent* was the only word that I could think of.

'I'm telling Miss Crowley and the police.'

'Tell them what, eh? If you want to see Miss Crowley

or the police, I'll take you there. I'll take you to both if you like. I'll just tell Mums to phone work and that we're going –'

'No, don't tell her or Gordon, please don't tell her.' I was pleading with him.

'You're talking rubbish, gurl. You're making no sense. Now Auntie Ada and Rosie are coming on Sunday, so I suggest you give Mums a hand to get the room ready!'

I ran into my bedroom, which I was to vacate once more, threw myself on that bed of last night's terror and sobbed. Could I have imagined it? Again the candle burned. No, you were 'topped', you were getting your just deserts, but, Mummy, I didn't mean to kill you, come back, forgive me, forgive me! I released a guttural scream into the white soft pillow and the candle went out.

I awoke to someone coming into the room: quickened breathing again followed by shuffling footsteps. The pillow was wet with my saliva. I turned my head fractionally and opened my eyes. Gordon and his father were placing a mattress against the wall, Auntie Ada's mattress – the evacuation had begun. I was afraid and yet also reassured that the unmistakable laboured breathing I'd heard in the darkness was now audible in the light, even increasing its pace as the chest of drawers was moved to join the wardrobe. I had not been mistaken. A later glimpse at my breasts showed bluey-mauve bruises deepening in hue. Yes, I'd been 'topped' all right, but why did he insist he would take me to Miss Crowley and the police?

By Saturday morning Auntie Ada's bed had been assembled and lay, its mattress bare, opposite mine. I provided myself with a box for my underwear and other items, and placed it on top of the dressing-table, ready for my move. My bedding had been put in the airing cupboard, less cumbersome than it had been at Christmas, although Mrs Oakes insisted I take two blankets, as the nights could be cold. I resolved that should I have any more night-time visitors while Auntie Ada and Rosie were here, I would scream blue murder, and envisaged going back to the East End of London to live with them. None the less, I was slightly apprehensive about staying in the lounge for the coming two weeks. It wasn't only fear of a further visit, but also an irrational fear of my brainchild, Mona the Myna.

Sunday morning left me drained. The day started extremely hot and I had to split another round with Jenny, the other paper-girl. I didn't finish until half-past ten. I put my bike away into the garage wearily. Blimp hadn't bounded up the garden to greet me. No one was in the kitchen or dining-room. I looked in the lounge, where the curtains were drawn back. The room smelled of Mansion Polish and roses, which Mrs Oakes must have picked from the garden. The myna bird's squawk, even though I was expecting it, still made me jump. Arthur Oakes had spent all Saturday talking to her and avoiding talking to me. Mona was his new hobby, I, his old. I looked out of the lounge window and my heart gave a jolt as I saw Izzie-Bon parked outside. Gordon must be in the house somewhere.

'I'm home!' I called out in the hallway. Silence hung over the house. 'I've left the papers on the dining-table.' Again there was a deathly hush. Nervously, I made my way upstairs and knocked on the Oakes's bedroom door. The bed was made, the room tidy but uninhabited.

Holding my breath, I knocked on Gordon's door. There was no sound from within and, my hands shaking, I turned the doorknob. To my surprise, it gave. Everything was as I remembered it, except that the eiderdown had been replaced by a blue-and-white cotton cover. A cream blanket and a white sheet were turned back and crumpled, as if a hasty departure had been made. Perhaps someone had had an accident, I thought, and then looked up at a large new picture of Adolf Hitler hanging on the wall above the bed. The Nazi flag had been draped over it in an artistic fashion, as if the Führer were taking a curtain call in Gordon's theatre of the Third Reich. I shuddered as Hitler's eyes followed me out of the room, a poignant smile playing on his lips. Why did he look almost kindly upon me? Was he a different Hitler down here than he was in London? Everyone there hated him and said he was evil, that he'd killed millions of people. Echoes of rhymes about him chanted in the playground came fleetingly into my head. There were no bomb-sites down here either. I shut the door quickly and went to my room.

That state of weariness that can engulf one, giving no choice but to sleep, overcame me as I opened my bedroom door, but my bedroom had gone. More roses from the garden sat on the dressing-table between two green glass ashtrays. My bed had found its twin again, and they were dressed identically in pink cotton bedcovers, which I hadn't seen before. I sat on Rosie's bed and cried. Any wish to lie down on this bed had gone. Then I realized that the Oakeses must have gone to pick up Auntie Ada and Rosie. A noise in the garden made me jump off the bed and run into the bathroom. I heard Mrs Oakes tell Blimp she'd get him some water. I splashed my face with cold water and went down to the kitchen. Mrs Oakes was waiting for the kettle to boil.

''Ello, ducks. Get a mug for yourself; I'm just making some coffee. I took him over to the park it was such a beautiful morning. I'm getting too old, though; he fair puffs me out. It's like an oven out there.'

'Yes, I know. I thought you'd all gone to collect Auntie Ada and Rosie from the station,' I yawned.

'We'd hardly have all got into the Hillman, would we? No, Dads has taken Gordon to look at a motor bike he's set his mind on, not that I agree with them. "You'll be selling it come winter," I told him, "we've been through this before", but he knows best,' she sniffed disapprovingly.

I took over the task of making the coffee and handed her a mug.

'Ooh, just the job,' she said smiling and putting the mug down.

I tried to stifle another yawn.

'Hey, look at the time! They'd best be back soon. Cuttin' it a bit fine to collect Ada and Rosie, and I'd better put this leg of lamb in. Forecast was rain, otherwise I wouldn't have done a roast. You look done for. Why don't you go upstairs and have a lie down? I've done the room ready. Mind you take them sandals off – I put clean bedspreads on.'

Feeling like a contrite Goldilocks, I refused.

'Why not go in the lounge if you don't want to mess the room up?' The incongruity of this statement was lost on her: no one could rival Auntie Ada and Rosie for messing up rooms. Suddenly I wanted to strike her, and this feeling of hatred and violence towards Mrs Oakes shocked me, shocked me into submitting to being shuffled into the lounge for 'forty winks' on the settee. Mona fluffed up her feathers and squawked as we entered the room. Leaning across the back of the settee, Mrs Oakes drew the curtains shut, and the bird stopped in mid-squawk.

'Go on, ducks, get your head down. Not looking forward to Auntie Ada and Rosie coming down, are you? Is that what's up, eh?'

'I don't mind,' I answered and, in view of what had happened three nights ago, I didn't.

'Wouldn't mind if I put a record on, would you? It's a soothing one, like. Only it came into my head in the park and I couldn't stop singin' it. I get like that an' I just have to hear it. Sure you won't mind? Like I said, it's a soothin' one.' Without waiting for an answer, she switched on the light, which made Mona start squawking again. Oh God, I couldn't bear Gordon Macrae singing 'Oh, What a Beautiful Mornin'' or about a surrey with fringes on top, and even the thought of 'Ado Annie's' song about being 'jest a gal who cain't say no' made me shudder.

'Got it!' Mrs Oakes exclaimed triumphantly, and I heard her turn the switch on the radiogram and the crackle as she placed the arm on the record. She switched off the light and sat in the armchair, the orange glow from the radiogram lighting the sweet-smelling room. A repetitious click was coming from the radiogram and, with a deep sigh, she drew herself out of the chair. 'Dads was playing "Mona Lisa" this morning. He wants the bird to sing it – he played it over an' over!'

I thought the bird only talked, but said nothing. Suddenly soft piano keys filled the room, playing a haunting introduction, and the deep, rich velvet voice of Nat King Cole began: 'A blossom fell, from off a tree, it settled softly on the lips you turned to me, the gypsies say, now I know why, a falling blossom only touches lips that lie. A blossom fell ...' Mrs Oakes sang the plaintive melody with Nat and I thought of Hitler's lips and the smile that I'd seen on them that morning. Then Mr Oakes, Mr Oakes's lips that lied ... I saw blossom cascading around him, pink and white blossom falling, burying him as they thickened like snowflakes, past his chin, mouth, nose and eyes until he was no more, the lips that lied stopped for ever by soft pink and white blossom. Mrs Oakes put the record on a second time. I was comforted to know that other people must have been through my experience, clever people who could put it into words, and I fell asleep as Nat sang on.

From that Sunday the lounge would become my refuge. It started with the safety of being in there with Mrs Oakes, and the orange glow and the pink and white blossoms. Later, I would sit in the darkened room with the radiogram's orange glow and a world of 78-inch records, which would become my friends, giving me succour in the years ahead.

'Go and tell her to shake a leg, Rosie, luv.' Mr Oakes's voice penetrated my sleep.

Heavy footsteps crossed the floor and there was a slashing noise to my left and right as the curtains were drawn and daylight assaulted my eyes.

'C'mon, you lazy bugger, dinner's ready.' Rosie's massive hands grabbed my bare ankles and pulled me off the settee. I landed on the floor with a soft bump. Another enormous hand grabbed mine and pulled me to my feet. The myna bird began squawking, but Rosie was kneeling on the settee, her weight causing it to tilt into the bay of the window.

''Ere, kiddo, take a butchers out there.'

I was still not fully awake and, dazed, joined Rosie on the tilted settee.

'Go-Go's gonna go, go, go, ain't 'e, eh?'

'Where, where's he going?'

'On that motor bike, ya daft cow.' She managed to pronounce the last word 'cayer'! 'Look, it's an AJS, an' thems 'ave got pow–er! I'm gittin' im t' take me fer a spin after me dinner, too bleedin' right I am!'

'You look nice, Rosie,' I lied. She looked even fatter in summer clothes, with mottled upper arms that wobbled whenever she moved. The bodice of her green-and-white striped dress seemed to be desperately endeavouring to restrain her breasts, pushing her cleavage up to her throat and making it look more like a huge backside than a bosom, and one glistening with perspiration. She wore a pink Alice band in her hair and matching pink lipstick. Her eyebrows seemed to have splayed out and I thought she'd put Vaseline on them, then realized it was perspiration.

'Don't look s'bad yerself, kid. Ooh, is this Unc's latest 'obby? We ain't stopped 'earin' about it. Reckons they can talk like 'umans, 'e do. Well, 'ere goes: fuck, fuck, fuck! Ooze a pretty boy, fuck, fuck, fuck. Go on. Don' fancy one o' them, eh? Shit, shit, shit, say shit now.'

'Come on, you girls, your dinner's getting cold.' Mrs Oakes's voice interrupted Rosie's elocution lesson. I had to wipe tears of laughter from my eyes, so intently had the myna been listening, its head on one side, and gazing at Rosie in rapt attention.

''Ello darlin'.' Auntie Ada sat at the dining-table,

perspiration and gravy adhering to her whiskers and around her mouth. 'Blimey you've grown! C'mon an' give yer Auntie Ada a big kiss.' Her knife and fork clattered to her plate and she swept her index finger around her upper denture to collect some spring cabbage that had ribboned its way around it. Popping the curled piece of leaf on her tongue, she swallowed it, the dentures bobbing downwards briefly as if in acknowledgement. Auntie Ada was wearing a white cotton dress with big cabbage roses printed on it. The roses under her arms had grown a deeper red from the sweat creeping from there towards her sternum. I bent to kiss her, and the smell of tom-cats that she emitted almost took my breath away, but kiss her I would and I did, accepting with her soft kiss on my mouth the perspiration and gravy that she'd generously given me too.

Everyone was seated except Gordon, and Mrs Oakes instructed us that 'it was getting cold' and to 'carry on without Gordon, as his was in the oven'. Four of us began our meal, but Auntie Ada, who had no time for such social graces, had nearly finished hers. When Gordon arrived, carrying his dinner plate on a tray, I could smell the Palmolive soap he'd used on his hands from where I sat, the sun burning into my back through the open french windows.

'Ooh, that were luverly. Could go anuvver one o' your dinners, Kaff, no trouble, gel.' Auntie Ada placed her cutlery on her plate, having chased the last of the gravy around with her knife and licked it clean. She belched loudly. 'Manners!' she said.

Gordon, who was sitting next to her, surrendered his dinner, claiming that he was too hot to eat a cooked meal and refusing his mother's offer to make him a salad. Auntie Ada quickly pulled his plate towards her with one hand while pushing her empty plate away with the other.

'You'll have some apple pie and cream now, Gordon, and I don't mean maybe, and you'll help wash up!' Gordon said he wanted to get back to his motor bike, his hobby. *Motor bikes, mynas and me*, I thought as I began to stack the used dinner plates with his help. Neither of us spoke as we went into the kitchen. Mrs Oakes came in and put a large apple pie and a jug of cream on a tray, glaring at her son, who mumbled something as he reluctantly followed her back into the dining-room.

'Ooh, thass better, they've been killin' me. I can't enjoy me food, see, Artie.' Auntie Ada was wiping the sweat from her face with the oven cloth Gordon had brought in. As I bent to remove her plate, she put her arm around my waist, saying 'Ta, darlin'.'

'You said you wanted some, son, and you'll sit there and eat it.'

'I'll sit here a bloody long time then, Ma, and I'm not a kid.'

'Now then, lad, don't you let me hear you swearing at your mother.' Mr Oakes jumped to his wife's defence.

Gordon got up and left the dining-room, his mother running after him. The front door banged shut and Mrs Oakes returned looking flushed but triumphant.

'Well, he won't be goin' nowhere now, will he? I've got the keys to his motor bike and Izzie.' She laid them beside her plate. 'He's doing the washing and wiping up, don't no one else even think about it. You can clear the table and put the kettle on, you girls, but no more!' she concluded.

It was as I was collecting the dessert dishes that I saw the reason for Gordon's sudden loss of appetite: dark tan gums and Auntie's brilliant smile sat between her and Gordon's place. I felt a little queasy myself.

'I can manage soft things like Kaff's apple pie, but the buggers give me gyp when I chews fings, like. See, Artie, gum boils it is.'

Rosie surprised me by coming out to the kitchen and putting on the kettle. I stacked the dishes ready for washing and wiped a tray, which Rosie set with six cups and saucers while I poured the tea into the pot. 'I got somefin' t' tell ya later on,' Rosie confided as we made our way into the dining-room.

'"Only 'ad these fer two years," I says t' the dentist, "an' it took me too bleedin' long t' git these t' fit me proper." Aah, luv 'em, 'ere's the kids wiv the tea. I'll put 'em back fer me tea.' There was a clacking noise as Auntie Ada twisted her head to one side then the other, replacing the tan-and-white teeth. 'Fags don' taste the same wivout 'em neever, I've said t' you, ain't I, gel?'

Auntie Ada and Rosie took cigarettes out of their packets and lit them in unison. Mr Oakes took a large glass ashtray from the sideboard and placed it in the middle of the table.

'Don't go on about yer teef no more, Mum. I've bought ya everyfin' they got in the chemist, right down to bleedin' teevin' powders, ain't I? You'll just 'ave t' 'ave some more, thass all there is to it!' Rosie appealed to her mother through the summer sun and smoke haze enveloping us.

'Luverly cuppa. Been 'avin' bad dreams then, darlin', 'ave ya?' I nodded. 'Tellin' ya somefin', thass wot dreams is doin'!'

'Telling her she's got a vivid imagination I think, Ada, don't you, gurl?'

I began to tremble. Something was wrong here and I couldn't think what. Then it struck me. I hadn't said or accused him of anything, so why would a request to see the old 'crow' and the police make him aware of what I'd 'imagined'?

'What did I imagine?' Emboldened by the presence of Auntie Ada and Rosie, and now wishing to God I'd told Pauline and she'd told Deirdre, I looked straight at him.

'It wasn't my nightmare. You tell me, gurl.'

'Artie, even if she could remember, and I'm blowed if I can, I don't think it's nice to go asking her, do you?'

A silence hung in the air, punctuated only by the rasping of the matches as Auntie Ada and Rosie lit fresh cigarettes.

'I'll just start the washing up,' I mumbled, noting that Mr Oakes was very flushed now and that his glasses had begun to travel up and down his nose at a furious pace. My mind was in a whirl and I was frightened.

'Are you listening to me, ducks? I said his lordship is to do the washing and wiping up. You can take the tea tray out; everyone's finished.'

'Eh, git us a cuppa coffee, kiddo, while you're out there, eh?'

'No, Rosie, she isn't here to wait on you. If you want a cup of coffee, you can make it yourself!' her aunt chided.

'Sorree,' Rosie said sarcastically, and jumped up, making the table tremble. 'We might as well do this lot an' sod 'er. She wouldn't let her darlin' boy git sore 'ands from washin' up anyways, silly cayer.'

Rosie and I worked together swiftly between her constant cigarettes. I wondered for a fleeting moment if I dared tell Rosie what had happened to me and then decided against it. After we tidied the kitchen Rosie stood at the kitchen door puffing at a cigarette while I made a tray of coffee for everyone.

''Ere, bring ours upstairs wiv ya, I got somefin' t' tell ya. I been dyin' t' tell ya since I got 'ere. I weren't gittin' bossy wiv ya when I asked ya t' make me some coffee – I wanted t' tell ya me news, see! I was gittin' ya out 'ere t' tell ya. C'mon le's go.'

Upstairs Rosie directed me to sit on Auntie Ada's bed. I had to climb over a suitcase that looked like it had been split in two, its entrails disgorged on the floor. With one enormous hand she swept aside the clothes strewn over the other bed and sat down with such weight that the mugs rattled and coffee spilt over the dressing-table. Rosie said to leave it, it'd dry in the sun.

'I've met this bloke, an 'e's bleedin' gorgeous, 'e really is. Ol' Willis the chemist pegged out in Febry – well, 'e was nearly seventy if 'e was a day – an' this bloke Charles takes over, don' 'e. 'E don' like bein' called Chas or Charlie; it's Charles.' Rosie was momentarily lost, savouring the name. 'Charles an' me, we're courtin' like, but don' tell no one, don' let it slip nor nuffin'. Promise me ya won't tell anyone. Not me mum, not Auntie, not Unc or Go-Go, specially not Bert, don' say nuffin' t' Bert. Promise?'

I promised, but Rosie wasn't content, I had to swear on the Holy Bible. I couldn't find my Bible but I had a scripture textbook in my satchel. I placed my right hand on it, promising not to tell any of the aforementioned people. My oath sworn, Rosie lit another cigarette and bounced again on the bed.

''Er, 'e's married like, but in name only. I mean, they never go to bed like.'

I had visions of a pharmacist and his wife staying up all night gazing at the huge glass jars, the red, green and yellow contents captivating them.

''E's got two kids, boys they are, thass all thass stoppin' 'im an me bein' tergevver right now. Anyways, 'e's tellin' 'er, 'is missus, like, while I'm down 'ere, that 'e's gotta 'ave a divorce 'cos I'm the only gel in the world fer 'im. 'E reckons 'e didn' know what love was till 'e met me. We're gonna git a 'ouse over Wimbledon way, and look!' Fishing in the cavernous depth of her cleavage, Rosie extricated a long silver chain. Attached to it was a band the size of a curtain ring with a solitary diamond the size, and almost the shape, of an ant embedded in it.

'Oh, it's beautiful, Rosie!' I declared.

'I know. Cost 'im a bleedin' bomb, it did an' all, but 'e just says I'm wurf every penny, bless 'im.' Another silence as Rosie was back in the arms of her Charles, a faraway look in her eyes. 'We're 'avin' free kids, a gel, then a boy, then anuvver gel. 'E likes yer name fer our first gel, so ya should be feelin' dead proud an' all.'

I told Rosie it was indeed a great honour to bestow upon me.

'I gotta write to 'im care of me mate Grace, an' e's gonna write 'ere an' address it ter you, then you can give 'em t' me on the QT. Ya don' mind, do ya?'

'No, I don't mind, Rosie. I meet the postman every morning coming back from my round, and I can slip them up to you when I get back in.' I did indeed feel privileged to be of assistance in Rosie's love affair.

'I knew ya would. I knew I could trust ya. I told me

mate Grace I could an' all. I want you an' Grace as me bridesmaids in powder blue. Oo! I'm so 'appy. I gotta try an' phone 'im t'night at the shop. You can go out fer a walk with me, like. I've seen me weddin' dress. It's a bleedin' dream.' Again Rosie was lost to a vision.

'I told 'im, I says, "Charles, we're doin' fings proper an ya'll 'ave t' wait till our weddin' night," but ya know 'ow it is . . . we got carried away a bit in the back o' the car. 'E's got a smashin' car. "Don't deny it, Rosie. Ya wannit, ya wannit as much as I do."' Rosie had been chattering on while the room filled with her cigarette smoke and my eyes stung, but now it was her words that stung, the very same words that Mr Oakes had used. I shivered in the heat of that July afternoon.

16

Rosie was lying on her bed telling me that she couldn't take the risk of having kids yet, but Charles had said he was like a boy scout – always prepared – and how it was a good job he was a chemist. I imagined him being like Mrs Oakes: 'pre-pare' had always been her advice on everything. I knew what Rosie was talking about and wanted to bring the topic around to a 'friend' of Pauline who'd experienced what I had with Gordon and Mr Oakes, but my attempts at speaking about anything that didn't involve Charles got little attention.

'Luv's a funny fing. I mean, them records Auntie plays all the time, ya know? I used t' fink they was dead soppy. Now they makes sense; funny that, ain't it? As fer yer mate's chum, if this neighbour's "done" 'er already an' rape's inevitable, tell 'er from me "Lay back an' enjoy it, kiddo."' Rosie found this extremely funny.

Rosie asked me 't' give 'er a 'and' tidying her things, so as she lay on the bed blowing smoke rings, I began to put her large underwear into my drawers. As I hung up her dresses and cardigans I remembered that night, the night of nightmares. Rosie had heard Mr Oakes say that I had a vivid imagination, but it was Rosie who'd told me all about the Oakeses and their hobbies, and me being one of them. I was hanging one pink and one blue plastic mac on the remaining hanger, my heart beating fast in my chest and the sweat from my hands making them stick to the see-through material. Without turning my head, I whispered loudly to Rosie, 'It wasn't Pauline's friend it happened to, Rosie, it was me, here in this room with your uncle, and in Gordon's room with Gordon, only Gordon . . .'

Silence. I knew as soon as the words were out I would be scared, but not this scared. I turned around slowly. Rosie was asleep, a cigarette burning down to her huge nutmeg-brown fingers. I took the cigarette from her and put it in the overflowing ashtray. 'Fuck you, Rosie, you fat horrible . . . horrible . . .' Rosie was snoring softly. I left the room, went into the bathroom, sat on the edge of the bath and cried. I wouldn't give her her letters from the postman; I'd rather throw them down the drain.

I went down to the kitchen. Gordon was making the salad he'd refused from his mother, putting cold meat and salad stuff on six plates. 'This bloody butter is like oil,' he complained. I didn't answer him. 'Well, everyone can have bread and oil with their tea,' he continued, mumbling.

'Are you doing everyone's tea then?' I asked, not looking at him.

'Yeah, it's like being back in the army.'

'I'll give you a hand with the bread and butter,' I offered, and proceeded to spread a piece of brown bread with the buttercup-yellow liquid.

'Wish I'd stayed in. It would've been better all round.' He was cutting the slices straight across instead of diagonally as his mother would have insisted.

'It's a bit hot to stay in all day,' I said after a long silence.

'No, I meant stayed in the army, signed up for twenty-five years. It would have been better all round. Sleep OK last night then? No more nightmares? Eh, you know, you scared me. I thought you'd had an accident or, uh, appendicitis or . . .'

I glanced at him surreptitiously and saw his head bent deeply into his chest. He was silently cursing the grease that covered his fingers as he placed the buttered bread on the plate.

'Better let you get back to your new motor bike. Do you like it?' I had washed up and tidied the kitchen and was about to exit through the kitchen door.

'Oh, it's really something. Needs a clean and new spark plugs but it's what I've always longed for. How about coming for a spin on it some time?' He coughed nervously, tucking his head even deeper into his chest.

'Oh no! No, thanks. I'd be too frightened!' The words were out before I could check myself. I realized I meant them.

'Yeah, eh . . . yes, of course. I wasn't thinking. Callie?' I wondered if this were some strange term of apology. 'Callie, I don't ever expect you to forgive me for . . .'

He was now looking at me and I at him, puzzled by this strange word 'Callie'. Candid blue eyes tried to hold mine, but I looked away. A tic on his left cheek was working furiously. I picked up the tea towel that I'd already folded and placed in the red rubber 'teeth' of yet another Ideal Home Exhibition gadget glued to the back of the kitchen door and dropped it. He moved forward, picked up the cloth and handed it back to me.

'Thanks,' I said, plunging the cloth back into the rubber teeth. The ambiguity of my thanks emboldened him to pursue the conversation and I heard him stumble on some words as I turned to leave the kitchen.

'Er, please, I know you'll always hate me but . . .' His hands were shaking and his words, stilted, tripping, stumbling, incoherent, spilled out. 'The other night I thought it was what . . . what . . . happened, I thought it could have brought on the nightmare. I was so afraid . . . they were the screams that you . . . and I didn't know what, so –'

'Did you think I had a nightmare the other night?' I interrupted.

'I thought it was, eh . . . I didn't know what to think, Callie. I thought . . . well, you know . . . I just . . . Why, is it important what I think?'

'No. But your father doesn't think it was a nightmare.'

'Yes, I gathered that, I've heard him. But . . . why ever not, why doesn't he think so?'

'I don't know. You'd better ask him.' I felt a sudden sense of what I can describe only as power, a feeling totally new to me, as I opened the kitchen door. He moved swiftly across the room and stood in the doorway. I found my eyes resting on the buttons of his shirt and suddenly felt trapped. He seemed to sense my fear and spoke in a voice loud enough to wake even the snoring Rosie.

'Will you think about going on the monster motor bike next week then, just around the block, eh?'

'No. I know who will though, Rosie will. She said Go-Go would really Go! Go! Go! now.'

'Oh God, I don't want to take her out.' He lowered his voice, ran his hands through his sparse grey hair and raised his eyes to the heavens.

'Did you leave your apple pie because of what Auntie Ada took out?' I asked suddenly, my voice also lowered.

He covered his face with both hands and dragged his palms and fingers down both cheeks. 'Oh God! They're so embarrassing, both of them.'

'What? The teeth?' I asked.

'Yes, those too!' His face suddenly lit with laughter and I laughed too. 'Sure you won't change your mind about going for a spin? We'll just go round the block, only ten minutes.'

'No, Gordon, thanks, I won't change my mind. By the way, what does "Callie" mean?'

'"Callie"? Oh, it's how I think of you ... I don't know why. It's a sort of nickname. I can only think of you as that now, Callie.' His voice broke off in a whisper.

What had he thought of me as before, before he smote me with his axe, before he 'tailed' me? I suddenly didn't want to be talking to this man any more. I didn't want to be in this kitchen, I didn't want to be in this house.

'I'm going to see Pauline, I'll be back for tea,' I called to him over my shoulder.

Pauline's father was snoring in his armchair, a Sunday newspaper covering his face, while her mum sat in the other, her head rolled to one side, arms folded as if her husband's rhythmic nasal grunts were a lullaby. Deirdre looked in.

'Come on, Derek's up here an' all. We'll have a party.' Deirdre and Derek were getting engaged next year.

'Pauline home?' I whispered, worried about waking her slumbering parents as Deirdre led me past their chairs and upstairs to the bedroom she shared with Pauline. I was sorry to have missed a chance to talk to Pauline's mum and dad. He always teased me and made me laugh, and she always made me feel important.

'What you whisperin' for? They won't wake till dead on seven, and, yes, Pauline's up here.' Deirdre mimicked my whisper and gave my arm an affectionate squeeze as we climbed the stairs.

In the bedroom Derek was sprawled across Deirdre's bed reading out Mary Grant's Problem Page.

'Hi, Sunshine! Come and listen to Deirdre's problems. She writes every week to this woman and she prints all her letters. Listen! "Dear 'D', if you really want to surprise your boyfriend Derek when he takes you to the dance this week and you want to add that bit of sparkle and mystery, go incognito, have a wash!"'

'You swine!' Deirdre was laughing and I was too, although I wasn't too sure what 'incognito' meant. I made a mental note to look it up in the dictionary Gordon had given me for Christmas. Deirdre was beating Derek around the head with the magazine and they were both laughing.

'Make yourself useful. Four coffees, waiter, please,' Deirdre said, giving her boyfriend one last playful slap on the head with the now battered paper. He put both hands up in mock surrender and left the room bowing and walking backwards, asking 'Black? White? Sugar?'

I finally noticed Pauline. She was seated in front of the dressing-table mirror. Her face was a light-grey colour, her eyes stared intently at me and her pink mouth pouted.

''Ow 'uch 'onger, Dee?' she asked, scarcely moving her lips.

'You look like Auntie Ada without her false teeth, Pauline. What's happened?' I asked.

''Eckles,' was the answer from the pursed lips.

'Only another hour, Paul, an' they'll have all gone.' Deirdre told her sister.

'An hour?!'

'No, go and wash it off, lukewarm water mind.'

Pauline flapped a hand at me and went off to the bathroom.

Deirdre laughed as she saw my puzzled expression. 'It says in this book lemon and Fullers Earth will get rid of freckles, so we're having a go.'

'Can I try it?' I asked eagerly, wanting to rid myself of the orangey spots sprinkled over my nose, spilling down on to my cheeks and arms.

'Sure. Let's see if it's worked on Sis, then I'll mix some more up. Oh, here's Derek with the coffee. There's a good boy.' Derek pretended to bark like a dog and Deirdre patted him on the head.

'Oh, Dee, look, they've not gone, they're worse!' Pauline wailed as she followed Derek into the room.

'Come here. Well, they look a bit lighter to me,' Deirdre reassured her.

'More of a donkey brown now, I'd say!' Derek came over and scrutinized Pauline's face.

'Pig!' Pauline put her tongue out at him. 'You can make me up now, Dee. Come on,' she wailed, then turned her attention to me. 'Frankenstein's wife and daughter arrived?'

I said they had indeed.

I watched for the next fifteen minutes while Deirdre applied a stick of make-up that made Pauline's freckles disappear. I wondered why Pauline had sat there for so long with a grey face when her skin could be transformed to an unblemished beige so quickly. Deirdre spat on a black block of mascara and applied it to Pauline's lashes. Faint strokes from the same brush accentuated her eyebrows, a flat round piece of lint gave her cheeks a pretty blush, and green powder was rubbed over each eyelid with deft fingertip strokes. A final touch of coral-coloured lipstick transformed Pauline from fairly attractive to beautiful, and she grinned at me in the mirror, knowing it. I smiled back, seeing myself as a freckled, piggy-eyed, plain Jane.

'Your turn. Sit,' Deirdre commanded and I took my place on the chair.

'Can I borrow some of your Amami? I want to set my hair, Dee?'

'Hair first, make-up afterwards, dummy. It'll all run, you know. It's a waste of make-up and my time, Paul. Oh, go on; you will anyway.' Deirdre gave her sister a good-natured smile and concentrated on my face.

The obliteration of my freckles took my breath away. Then I became sleepy under the soft stroke of Deirdre's fingers.

'No, I'll use brown on you, black'll be too dark.' She spat and made a muddy pool on the block of mascara, working it to the required thickness with the miniature brush and darkening my lashes. Blue powder was applied to my eyelids, and soft strokes of colour on my cheeks made my face glow. Deirdre applied my lipstick. 'It's lighter than Paul's. It's called Sari Peach. It really suits you,' she told me.

I was drowsy when she made a final feather touch on my eyebrows with the tiny brush.

'Right, you can look now – da-da!'

I looked in the mirror and couldn't believe it was me. 'Oh, Deirdre, I look so . . . so different.' I didn't want to say pretty in case she thought I was vain. A loud wolf-whistle came from the bed where Derek was slumped reading a Western.

'Not different, beautiful, doesn't she, darling?' Deirdre glanced across at her boyfriend, then brought her eyes back to my face in the mirror and smiled broadly at me.

Pauline appeared at the door, her hair covered in pin-curls secured with kirby-grips and smelling of the Amami setting lotion. Lines of black ran from her eyes to her chin.

'Oh, see! I told you, you look really lovely, doesn't she, Dee?'

'Aw, no, Pauline, not lovely, not me. You did . . . er, do.'

'"Who me? Me a swan? Aah, go on . . ."' Derek sang Danny Kaye's song. I had a fleeting memory of my mother singing it, and I wanted to stay in this house with these lovely people for ever.

'Who me? Me a badger? Aw, but I'll 'ave yer . . .' Derek was looking at Pauline now.

'What?' whined Pauline.

'Look at your face! You look just like a badger, take a look at yourself in the lake. "An' she looked, an' she saw an' she said, 'I am a Badger.'"'

Pauline saw her mascara markings in the mirror and threw a hairbrush at Derek, missing him.

'Aw, Dee, tell him he's not funny. He's always taking the mick! I'm fed up. Tell him, Dee!'

'Pack it in, Derek, you'll wake Mum and Dad up. You know he loves teasing you, Paul; don't take any notice of him. Come on, let's take this off.' Deirdre wiped the mascara from Pauline's cheeks with cold cream and cotton wool and reapplied her make-up.

'Pig,' Pauline repeated to Derek, make-up and beauty restored.

'Badger,' retorted Derek. This caused a pillow fight, which left Pauline once again without lipstick, but with plenty on the pillowcase.

'Stop that row, you kids. S'posed to be our day of rest!'

'That's it. You've woken Mum up, you two. Hey, don't look so scared. She won't bite, she's soft our Mum, she really is. Take the coffee cups down with me and you two tidy up the room,' Deirdre ordered her sister and boyfriend.

Both of Pauline's parents were awake when we got downstairs, and, between yawns, expressed delight at seeing me.

'Our Dee's had a 'and in makin' the future Miss World, I can see. Looks like the fairy off the Christmas tree, don't she, Mother?' Pauline's dad smiled and told 'Miss World' to take her throne. I sat on the settee.

'She does that, Dad. Not so heavy on the eyebrows, Dee, she's too dark around the eyebrows ... that's better, she looks pretty as a picture. Our Paul done up as well, I s'pose?'

'Course, Mum, only she's had a pillow fight with Derek, the usual with those two. Don't worry, they're tidying the bedroom, be down now. You've put the kettle on, Mum? Sit down, I'll make it.' Deirdre went into the tiny kitchen.

'Your auntie and cousin down from London, are they, my love?'

I replied that they were, then Pauline and Derek came in.

'Two beauty queens on our hands, Mother,' Pauline's dad proclaimed as Deirdre returned with a tray of cups and saucers.

'Oh thanks, Dad! What does that make me then?'

'The fairy queen and her two princesses,' he chuckled.

Derek led Deirdre over to the mirror that hung above the fireplace.

'Mirror, mirror on the wall, who's the fairest of them all?' he asked, pushing Deirdre's face closer to the glass. Suddenly he made a loud noise like a whiplash, KER–ACK!

'Go and get the tea; it's brewed by now. Go on, get out!' Deirdre was laughing as she pushed Derek towards the kitchen.

The aroma of oranges, apples, peaches and pears, mixed with onions and cucumbers wafted into the lounge from the lean-to next to the kitchen that housed boxes of market produce. After we'd drunk our tea, Pauline's mum went out into the kitchen and brought everyone a dish of strawberries and cream. For the second time that afternoon I wished I could live here.

As I was helping Pauline and her mother with the dishes I took out my hankie and wiped the cream from around my mouth. I baulked when I saw the brown and orange stain on the hankie.

'Oh, Pauline, I've got to go, I'm late already, and I can't go with this on. Will it come off?' Panic was rising in my voice.

'Course it will, soppy date, and even if it didn't, what harm's a bit of make-up do? All young girls do it. Some people have funny ideas and if you want my opinion, those people –'

'Come on upstairs. It'll only take a mo' to come off.' Deirdre had interrupted the comments about the Oakeses I was sure her mother was about to make and escorted me up to the bedroom, Pauline at her heels.

While she applied the cold cream and rubbed it off with cotton wool, Deirdre told her sister and me, not for the first time, that we really ought to do the commercial course at school. She was a secretary and had a really good job. 'You'd never be out of work with short-hand, typing and commerce behind you.' She seemed to be having some trouble getting the make-up off and applied a third layer of cold cream. 'There, it's all gone, look. I'm serious about you doing that course. It'll stand you in good stead. Close your eyes. That's it!'

The make-up had all gone but my lips looked red, as red as they'd looked when Gordon had ground them round and round. I blinked back the tears. I wanted to beg them to let me stay, but they all came out to see me off and the bike wobbled its way down the street as they stood on the pavement waving. I gave one last wave as I turned the corner. Looking skywards, I said aloud, 'Why are you doing this to me, God?' The orange flame flickered and my tears raced to put it out.

17

I dreaded going back into that house. I put my bike away, walked slowly up the path and, giving my lips a final wipe with the handkerchief, into the kitchen, where Auntie Ada and Mrs Oakes were making the two pots of tea and laying out the scones and sponge cake I'd made. I felt guilty as I looked at them, but Auntie Ada's warm greeting dispelled such feelings.

''Ere she is then. See yer pal, did ya darlin'?'

I said I had and should I lay the table? Mrs Oakes said I was too late, that Auntie Ada had done it, and the cold meat that Gordon had put out with the salad had gone dry and curled, and shouldn't I have known better, as he said I'd given him a hand.

'Sorry,' I said.

'If there's one word I can't stand, Ada, it's sorry!' she sniffed.

I wandered into the dining-room, where the plates of salad lay, colourful nests of green lettuce and watercress, cucumber and red tomato slices, cerise radish waterlilies I'd made earlier that morning, and hoops of white onion rings. Pink slices of ham curling like a carpet, dark pink-and-cream doormats of speckled corned beef, edges flat but maroon in colour, blushing as if in disgrace. Mr Oakes was seated at the dining-table studying his birthday book on myna birds. He looked up briefly as I came in and responded to my hello with a brief grunt and a look that made me feel very uneasy.

The sound of a harsh engine and a throttle at full thrust made me jump. A commotion at the door heralded Rosie's shrieks of laughter. Her hair was dishevelled and her cheeks crimson.

'Oh, Go-Go, I didn' mean it. ''onest injun, I did'n', Go-Go!' More shrieks of laughter. Gordon followed her in, a deep scowl on his face. 'Oh Mum, Auntie, we must've done a ton at least. It was bleedin' fantastic an' 'e says, "Put yer arms round me, Rosie an' 'old tight!" I didn' mean t' 'old 'is "ol' boy".' Rosie staggered against the cupboard under the stairs, hysterical with laughter. Mrs Oakes didn't look amused, though Auntie Ada did.

'Oh Rosie, Rosie, wot a gel. You ain't upset 'im again, 'ave ya? 'As she, darlin'? C'mon an' give yer ol' auntie a cuddle, boy, she don' mean no 'arm. C'mon, ya can't go round wiv a face as long as that now.'

'Ooh, 'is fing's longer than 'is face, Mum!' Rosie squealed.

'That's enough, Rosie! Gordon, the little 'un and myself, we don't want to hear any more of your soot,' Mrs Oakes admonished.

Gordon rushed up the stairs two at a time. 'It's smut, not soot, Ma,' he called over the banisters.

'Same difference, boy, and don't ask me to stick up for you again, 'cos I won't, and I don't mean maybe. Tea's ready and I'm not having dinner-time's performance from you. The cold meat's ruined!' Her voice rose higher as Gordon ascended to his Hitler room.

At eight o'clock Rosie said it was time she had some exercise and we would take Blimp for a walk. I waited with Blimp, having walked up and down the road five or six times before stationing myself firmly outside the telephone box. Blimp spent several pennies up against the box and Rosie spent even more, her babbling punctuated with the 'crunch' and 'ting' as she continually pressed button A. Gordon passed us on the motor bike on our way back, but either didn't see us or chose not to.

Mr and Mrs Oakes and Auntie Ada were in the lounge playing 'Mona Lisa' over and over again. The myna bird looked positively bored.

During the following fortnight there were day trips to Bognor Regis, Brighton and Chessington Zoo. I would come back from my newspaper round and help Mrs Oakes prepare the picnic food and the thermos flasks. We'd all pile into the Hillman, Mr and Mrs Oakes in the front, Auntie Ada and me in the back, with a hamper between us and Blimp seated uncomfortably on the floor. Gordon, with Rosie his pillion passenger, would show off, racing past us on the motor bike, Rosie's skirts billowing out to reveal voluptuous thighs while her large arms encircled Gordon's waist.

All the same, Rosie was having problems. Two of her attempts to get through to Charles on the telephone had been abortive. She also accused me of stealing her mail. I began to wait for the postman, praying there would be a letter with a London postmark addressed to me. The day before she was due to return to London she had telephoned Charles, only to find that he had not yet told his wife about 'his one and only love'. He swore he had written to her every single day. Her fury knew no bounds and that night Rosie and her uncle had a field day with me.

I'd arrived home for dinner late, as a paper-boy had

left and I and another boy had had to share his round. Heavy drizzle had begun to fall half-way through the round and it had grown cold. Mrs Oakes had sympathized with her son over Auntie Ada's teeth, so he usually ate before the rest of us, and joined us later for a cup of tea. Mrs Oakes gave him the all clear as soon as Auntie's teeth gave the final clacking signal that they were laid to rest on her pink gums. So this evening I was ushered to Gordon's seat and a plate with a spongy omelette, chips and peas was set in front of me next to Auntie's orange 'pastry cutters'. The ones I took to be the lower dentures, shaped like a horseshoe, clinked at the side of my plate as Auntie Ada flicked away the ash that had dropped on to the tablecloth. Reluctantly, I put my knife into the soft belly of omelette and bit into the yellow egg. The orange-and-white teeth were grasped and Auntie's gums drew them into their resting place with a final crisp click. She belched loudly and lit a fresh cigarette from the red glowing end of the one she had been smoking.

'Manners! 'Ere, ya should've dried yer 'air before ya sat down, darlin'. Cold in the 'ead, bring on brain fever, an' yer gorn, just like that.' She snapped her forefinger and thumb. 'A killer that brain fever is.'

'Well it's warm in here and she's not exactly dripping. Eat up, ducks, there's a good girl.'

Auntie Ada's smoke billowed in my direction, as did Rosie's. Just as I was beginning to think that the Genie of the Lamp might appear, Gordon came in, wet through.

'Go straight upstairs and change out of those clothes, Gordon. I'll put the kettle on. D'you all want coffee? C'mon now, Rosie, give me a hand.'

Rosie pouted but did as her aunt bade. Auntie Ada went out with them, saying she was washing up and no mistake. I was left alone with Mr Oakes, who again picked up his book on mynas and, without looking at me, said, 'Gordon'll want to sit there.'

I picked up my plate and took it to my usual place. I chewed hard and tried to swallow the meal, but it was like rubber and there seemed to be a constriction in my throat. The rain was slashing like a cut-throat razor at the windows behind me. I felt I should say something but I couldn't. All at once everyone crowded back into the dining-room and a wave of relief swept over me.

'Young man, you shouldn't have gone on that bike in this weather. The little 'un was wet, but you were saturated.'

'It wasn't raining when I went out, Ma,' Gordon countered.

His father and Rosie were giggling. 'So ya reckon that bird o' yours, Unc, is sayin' "Mona Lisa"?' she asked.

I noticed that Rosie was wearing a virginal white shirtwaister dress and thought idly that she must have purchased all this white apparel during her stay. I certainly hadn't put it away when they arrived. I was glad she didn't make any attempt to speak to me. I didn't want to have anything more to do with her, especially since she'd accused me of having stolen the letters from her drippy Charles.

'Wot ya got round yer ears, gel? Ya got earache again? Them muffs ain't gonna do ya no good, gel. Ya wants some o' that Camflagated oil an' bung 'em up wiv a bit o' wadding, don't she, Kaff?' Auntie Ada looked to her sister-in-law for confirmation.

I looked up at the 'invalid' at the same time as Mrs Oakes and Gordon did. Rosie's dressing was elaborate for an earache – a white lacy band, partly buried in the thick dark hair with two white lace-edged pads over each ear. It appeared to be fastened at the back of her neck.

''Ere, I say, ya don' wanna go gittin' them "master-oids" round yer ear'oles, gel...'

'Rosie!' Get that off your head this very minute, and I don't mean maybe!' Mrs Oakes's voice was low, almost menacing. 'Now, Rosie!'

By this time Gordon, his mother and I had given Rosie our undivided attention. Mr Oakes was laughing heartily, arms crossed, holding his ribs and rocking to and fro. Tears coming down his cheek forced him to release his grip on his ribs and take his glasses off to wipe his eyes and the misted lenses. Rosie, and her uncle's uncontrollable laughter, made me want to laugh too. I'd never seen Mr Oakes laugh like that before. More guffaws as she ripped the 'dressing' from her head. It was then, to my horror, that I saw it was one of my bras. She was holding the garment up, a massive finger and thumb pinching the cups of the white cotton and flimsy lace underwear that I'd been so proud to own.

'What's she gonna put in them, eh? Them's even too small fer me bleedin' ear'oles!' Rosie and Mr Oakes burst out in more uncontrollable laughter.

'Rosie, how dare you!' Mrs Oakes was furious.

My face was burning and I snatched the garment from Rosie's enormous, ugly hands and squeezed past her and Auntie Ada. Tears blinding me, I headed for the door.

'You make me sick, you two. No wonder no bloke's ever . . .'

Those were the last words I heard as I made my exodus, a sob escaping from my throat. I could hear Gordon's voice growing louder. Rosie was shouting too, but it was Mrs Oakes's 'holler', as she used to call it, that finally quelled the noise.

I sat on the toilet, wiping my tears with the object of Mr Oakes's and Rosie's mirth. I wished he and Rosie were dead. I wished I were dead. I got up, took the aspirin bottle from the bathroom cabinet, shook out four pills, and then an extra one to make sure, and swallowed them with tap water, making a cup with the palm of my hand. 'It is dangerous to exceed the stated dose' the bottle said. It seemed more dangerous not to now.

Mrs Oakes knocked on the bathroom door. Reluctantly, I opened it, quickly replacing the aspirin bottle in the cabinet first.

'Come on, luv, don't go cryin' over her. Have a lie down in my bed. She'll be gone tomorrow.'

And so will I Mrs Oakes, so will I.

Mrs Oakes pulled back the covers on the huge double bed and told me to lie on 'her' side. I could hear Gordon in his room next door and wondered what they'd all do when I didn't wake up. I wondered if I'd go straight to heaven. I felt a desperate, urgent need to see Gordon and tell him what I'd done. My stomach began to ache and I felt sick. The world had grown too old for me and I felt sure that Mummy would be waiting for me . . .

I awoke to a green-shadowed room with light

penetrating through the curtains. Someone was lying beside me. A regular crunching sound, like footsteps on gravel, came from my bedmate. Summoning my courage I glanced over and saw the glint of curlers. The crunching sound was Mrs Oakes grinding her teeth. A feeling of relief engulfed me, but I instinctively moved towards the edge of the bed. I was wearing my pants and a full-length petticoat. I touched my 'top' and 'tail': no pain, only a soreness in my stomach, a deep ache in my throat and tightness around my eyes. I saw my blue-and-white striped dress draped over a chair along with the white cardigan I had been wearing the night before. The night before ... Slowly memory edged its way into my consciousness like the dawn breaking, very slowly. I remembered the bathroom, the bottle of aspirin, and fear sprang out at me, fear coupled with immense relief. I was alive – how could I be? I swung my legs gently off the bed and collected the dress and cardigan. I glanced at Mrs Oakes, her white hair mingling with the whiteness of the pillowcase, the silver curlers like spiky icicles. I opened the bedroom door quietly and crept across to the bathrom.

I changed into my corduroy trousers and jumper and my other bra, taking them from the boxes in the airing cupboard. My eyes were swollen around the lids, so I splashed my face with cold water, then cleaned my teeth. I looked into the bathroom cabinet: the bottle of aspirin was still there, and I was still here. I went downstairs to the kitchen and let Blimp out. I put the kettle on to boil and put a spoonful of coffee and sugar into a mug, stirring the brown-and-white mixture and still puzzling over how I could have survived. True, my head ached a little, but I only felt as I did when I'd had a bad cold. I was sipping the coffee when I suddenly heard the kitchen door creak. I jumped and banged the mug down on the open flap of the kitchen cabinet, spilling coffee on to the white enamel surface.

'Pleased with yourself, are you, gurl, the row you caused here last night, eh? eh?' Without his glasses he stared at me in an unseeing way. He wore crumpled grey trousers and a white vest.

A deep sigh issued from my throat and my hands shook, but all at once I remembered Rosie and him and my bra and something tore my bowels with an almighty force, soaring through my chest and throat, pushing at my vocal cords until the words 'Drop dead' sounded loud and clear. I was no longer shaking, but I saw him blanch and tremble as he shuffled from the kitchen.

It was not he who was to drop dead, however, but Auntie Ada, in mid-December, just as I was about to prepare for the biannual evacuation from my room.

18

The loss I felt for Auntie Ada was great. Not only had she been the nearest thing to my grandmother, but her death seemed to provide the explanation for Granny's silence: she too must be dead. I cursed aloud at God and at death, who seemed so readily to pluck people I loved from me. Immediately, I asked forgiveness for my anger, in case I lost yet more.

After the funeral a very much changed Rosie came and stayed until the end of January. Rosie, who'd seemed to look life straight in the eye, could not begin to face death. I felt a great sadness and protectiveness towards her. She had said that she would sleep on the settee, but I insisted on occupying it as usual. It did not occur to me, or to Mrs Oakes, that Rosie might not want to sleep in the room she had so long shared with her mother.

Every evening I made my way downstairs, armed with my winter bedclothes, to the room I now loved. Here a whole new world of music opened up to me, the magical world of the '20s, '30s and '40s captured on those heavy, black, waxed discs. I listened to Jack Hylton and his orchestra; Roy Fox; Frank Sinatra singing 'All or Nothing at All', with Tommy Dorsey's band; and Ambrose and his orchestra playing 'Whistling in the Dark'. Al Bowlly sang 'Got a Date with an Angel' and 'I'll Do My Best to Make You Happy' with Ray Noble's band. The Mills Brothers sang 'When Deep Purple Falls over Sleepy Garden Walls', and Jessie Matthews performed 'Dancing on the Ceiling', 'A Room with a View' and 'Someone to Watch over Me'. The last was to become almost a hymn to me – 'I'm a little lamb who's lost in a wood, I know I could always be good, to one who watched over me' – as was Bing Crosby's rendering of 'Black Moonlight'.

I learned all the lyrics. The supply seemed endless and my appetite insatiable for this place where 'beyond the blue horizon lay a beautiful day'. This world that I had discovered was young and happy, and here I felt I 'belonged'.

Rosie, who had been extremely withdrawn throughout her stay of over a month, had succumbed to her grief during the annual Christmas Eve soirée with the Knightleys, when the full impact of her new-found status as an orphan seemed to hit her. I was familiar with this feeling of being 'one alone' (as John Hanson had sung so many times), an outcast, not belonging. I felt my throat constrict and tears well in my eyes for Rosie, and I touched her hand. It was 'Bert the Bobby', much to his wife's consternation, who took it upon himself to escort the loudly weeping Rosie from the lounge and up to my bedroom to 'let her get it out of her system', as he put it. When Rosie's ugly sobs subsided, Mrs Knightley went upstairs, a trifle wobbly on her feet after so many sherries, to ensure that that was all her husband was extracting from Rosie's system!

On Boxing Day morning I found myself alone in the lounge with Rosie. I felt genuinely concerned for her and asked if Charles would look after her. Rosie turned her back on me and I realized I'd committed a *faux pas*, as, her head bent down, she spoke into Mona's cage.

'Charlie is a bastard, a bastard, a bastard. Charlie's wife's in the fuckin' puddin' club, puddin' club, puddin' club, she's in the fuckin' puddin' club, an' Charlie is a bastard, a . . .'

The myna bird, having listened to Rosie's tale of woe (sung tunelessly to 'Charlie is My Darling') with her head on one side, eventually assessed the situation and said in a voice that was unmistakably Mr Oakes's, 'Mona Lisa, ha! ha!'

All was not lost for Rosie in the romance stakes, however. She confided in me that Bert was still in love with her, but she'd got another string to her bow, a rep called Bill, who'd taken a big shine to her. This, she informed me, ''ad riled Charles sumfin' rotten' and she was seeing Bill 'regular like'. I learned that Grace was to move in with her 'fer appearances', as she put it. My thoughts and hopes were for Bill . . . 'and then along came Bill, an ordinary guy . . .' Helen Morgan's sweet voice from my secret world of music rang in my ears. It was the last time the old Rosie reared her head, and for the remainder of her visit she stayed at a remove. No one could doubt that the grief she felt at her mother's death was anything but genuine, and I was sure, as I kissed her goodbye on that January morning, that she feared returning to her old home and new status.

Mrs Oakes had started working full time at Murray's with the commencement of the January sales. Thus I found myself once again coming home at lunch-time to feed Blimp and prepare the vegetables if I hadn't had time to do so before leaving for school in the morning. I would also lay the table for the evening meal. Mrs

Oakes would always make me sandwiches for lunch the evening before, and on the days when I had already prepared the vegetables I would make myself some coffee and take my meal into the lounge. The orange glow of the radiogram gave me enough light to select the records I wanted to listen to while I sat on my haunches, sipping coffee and eating Mrs Oakes's sandwiches. The record that captivated me on the day of Rosie's departure was 'You and the Night and the Music' played by the Debroy Somers Band. I was listening intently for the second time, absorbing the lyrics, when there was a shuffling at the door. It opened and Gordon was standing there in his pyjamas. The cheese scone I was about to bite jerked sideways, but my mouth remained open. I quailed. The vocalist, unaware that the world had stopped turning for me, spun on.

'Hi! I've got a cold or flu or something.'

'Eh, shall I get you some coffee and aspirin or . . .?'

'No, cheers anyway, I had some at twelve. Eh . . . Rosie, Rosie made one hell of a noise when she was going . . . I heard the music and . . .'

'I'm sorry, I didn't know, I thought you were at work, I wouldn't have woken you.'

'No, no, I was awake. Eh . . . I didn't know you went for this old sort of music, Henry Hall and all that . . . eh . . . Elvis the Pelvis I'd have thought would have been more your . . .'

'No, I like some of it, I like Elvis too, I . . .' I was uncomfortable.

'God, there must be hundreds there.' He tapped the shelves with a slippered foot. Most of the records were in buff sleeves, with a few colourful ones. 'I like that one, the one you just played.'

'Yes.'

'When I was young I used to like . . .' He shuffled across to the shelves to invade my world, just as his hero Hitler had invaded. I felt angry as he began to leaf through the covers. A triumphant noise and I heard the rustle of a record being removed from its sleeve. He took 'You and the Night and the Music' off the turntable and laid it on top of the radiogram. 'Here, "Echo of a Song". You'll like it.'

'The echo of a song you used to sing, when hearts were young and everything . . .' Al Bowlly was reminiscing to the room at large as Gordon turned up the volume. '. . . was one long summer's day when you were there,' Gordon sang along with the record. To my surprise, he had a remarkably good voice.

I placed the coffee and untouched scones on the occasional table and started to get up. 'It's nice, but I'll be late. I've got to do my bedroom now Rosie's gone and – '

'Callie, look, I want to tell you how I feel about you. It's real. I mean I really love you.' He was holding me by the forearm and I didn't want to upset him by pulling away.

'I've got to go, Gordon, please!'

It wasn't happening. *Please God make this all a dream, why didn't anyone warn me he would be at home. Rosie, oh God, Rosie, why did you go? GOD, MAKE HIM LET GO OF MY ARM HE'S PULLING ME DOWN WHY AM I ASKING YOU, GOD? IF YOU HATE ME THIS MUCH THEN I HATE YOU EVEN MORE, GOD, EVEN MORE THAN GORDON, GOD, EVEN MORE THAN SATAN, GOD.*

*

'Please, please don't, Gordon. Please, let me go.' My head gently bumped the rug by the hearth. I was crying now, rolling my head away from him. He was kissing the salty tears on my cheek.

'Callie, shush ... I'm not going to hurt you. Don't, please don't cry, I won't hurt you. Shush now.'

'Gordon, let me get up. I'll ... I'll be late. Pauline will be ...'

He was on his knees. One arm was across my shoulder, his other hand cupped under my head – a pillow or 'the block'? He was kissing my tears, his porous lips absorbing the salty water but unable to stanch the flow.

The echo of a song ... 'My Melancholy Baby' ... I'd never heard that song in this room or in this house. No! Let Mummy kiss it better ... Melly-Colly Baby ... one of Mummy's songs, her laughter kissing away the tears, me her 'Melly-Colly' Baby. Why am I your Melly-Colly Baby, Mummy? Her brown eyes laughing, delighted at my attempt at the word melancholy, then finally sliding off her lap with 'all gone, all better, Melly-Colly baby'. Echoes from a long ago and far away time ...'

'Don't be afraid, little one. I love you, I won't hurt you. Shush ... shush now, Callie.'

My body taut now as if in rigor, I turned my head away from the light of the radiogram. The hand that had cupped the back of my head I now knew to be the 'block'. It moved, attempting to wrest my head so that he could see my face. He gave up the struggle as again and again I twisted my head away from him, away towards the armchair, where my eyes became fixed on a walnut trapped beneath it. My body, which had put up a valiant fight, now failed against the weight that was placed fully upon it. My head and eyes, eyes fixed on the walnut, would be my strength. I heard his breathing quicken. A last violent effort from me as his hands thrust my navy-blue knickers down past my knees found my hand trapped under the small of my back. A shoe, or maybe it was my foot, fell on to the floor. My free arm lay across my breasts, locked as firmly as my head was. I tried locking my legs as tightly, but the axe-man prised them apart.

I waited. My eyes held the walnut; look at the walnut! My legs and buttocks were cold, cold and hard as the walnut's shell. With what seemed an even greater shock than before, the hard, hot instrument bit into me . . . nine, ten, twenty times the axe struck and all the while I watched the walnut. The walnut had been harvested from a strong mature tree. The tree was felled. It lay heavily on the sapling; the sapling had been crushed.

'Oh God, Callie! I'm sorry. I love you, I'm sorry, please, I'm sorry . . .' the axe-man lamented and, with a sense of incredible relief, I felt the crushing weight lift. Still I lay there. Cold, cold air permeated my body; my hand, at a tortuous angle under the small of my back, was numb. I lay still, listening to the axe-man and watching the walnut. I was no longer crying. Sap was oozing out of me, wet and sticky, on to the back of my school skirt and the rug, and still I lay there, not even bothering to cover the wound. I heard him get up and, whimpering, shuffle from the room. I turned my face away from the walnut. The orange glow from the radiogram's light seemed harsh on my eyes. I realized I was too late for school, and the thought didn't seem strange.

I got up slowly and pulled up my knickers. The cheese scones and cold coffee still stood on the small table, mute witnesses to what had taken place. An animal sound, that of a wounded beast, came from the kitchen. Blimp? Or . . .? The whimpering continued, the radiogram buzzed, its orange glow once my warm friend, the black disc with its reddish-brown label portraying the dog listening to His Master's Voice.

'Mona Lisa, ha! ha!' The myna bird's voice made me jump and move into sluggish action. I turned off the radiogram and the room became dark. I picked up the mug and plate. A strange keening was still coming from the kitchen. I limped into the dining-room and set the coffee mug and scones on the dining-table and made my way up to the bathroom. I was sore and bruised inside, but my sides didn't hurt as much as they had the first time.

Locked inside the bathroom, I ran a bath, throwing in two cubes of bath salts and a large splash of Dettol. The sap continued to run down my legs. My clothes were still in their boxes from Rosie's stay, and I reached into the airing cupboard for my corduroy trousers and the apple-green jumper, the last thing Auntie Ada had made for me. From my smaller box I took some clean blue knickers and a white bra with a blue bow, which I'd proudly purchased myself, and a clean pair of white socks. I turned off the taps. The bath water seemed hot to my touch, which it never was, but then my body had never felt as frozen as it did now.

I knew as I took off my blouse, school jumper and bra that there would be no visible wounds. After the first rape there could be no other. I undid my skirt, and as it fell to the floor I saw, with horror, that my legs and socks were covered in blood. I'd been wearing only one shoe too and hadn't noticed until now. The bright flash of crimson on my socks was a far duller shade on my navy knickers and school skirt. I looked around for some means of setting light to these garments, the garments of my guilt and shame, and put the hem of my skirt into the mouth of the geyser, but instead of igniting, it snuffed out the flames. Turning the knob on the white-enamelled gas water-heater, I realized I had extinguished the pilot light too.

Gingerly, I stepped into the bath. My legs felt stiff and cold with their rusting blood. Lowering myself into the water, I watched it turn a deep red, which spread and diluted until I found myself sitting in a sea of pink. I scrubbed hard at my body, the metallic smell of blood seeming to override that of the violet-scented bath salts and disinfectant. I jumped when Gordon rapped at the bathroom door.

'Callie, Callie, have I hurt you? Please, please tell me. Oh God, answer me, for God's sake, answer. Callie! I'll have to break the door down if you don't answer me. Callie, what have you done? Jesus Christ, what have you done?' His voice was a shrill scream.

What had *I* done? he was asking over and over. Yes, what had I done? I knew I had committed a sin, a terrible sin, with him, something on a par with what I'd done to Mummy. It was at that point, as I sat there shivering in that cold pink bath, that I realized that it was me and only me who was responsible for Mr Oakes 'topping' and Gordon 'tailing' me. I had caused it beyond any doubt. At no time, as I sat there listening to Gordon beseeching me to tell him what I had done, did it occur to me that he feared that I had committed suicide.

I got out of the bath and as soon as he heard me splashing my bloodstained clothing in the bathwater, he said in a calmer, strangled voice, 'I'm sorry, Callie. Are you hurt?'

Still I didn't answer him. I heard him go to his Hitler room and close the door. I washed my socks, skirt and knickers and took them downstairs to hang on the washing line. I heard him go into the bathroom. It was beginning to smell of gas as I left it, and I hoped he'd blow up if he tried to relight the geyser.

I went into the dining-room, took the cheese scones and coffee mug from the dining-table, gave the scones to Blimp and threw the coffee down the sink. Putting on the kettle, I made myself a cup of hot coffee. I was bruised and could feel the warmth of the blood flowing on to the sanitary towel. Suddenly I rushed, with my hand over my mouth, towards the kitchen door to make for the bathroom and, realizing it would be too late, was violently sick down the kitchen sink. I stood over the sink, my breath coming in short gasps, my hands trembling. It was only when I started to scrub the sink with Vim that I began to cry.

I laid the table and, taking my paper-round jacket from its peg in the hall, went out across the park and sat shivering on a bench. 'You and the Night and the Music' seemed to have gained a great significance in my repertoire of magical music, and even now I cannot bear to listen to this song, which had once enraptured me. Crosby's 'Black Moonlight', however, was, and still is, pressed in my book of remembrances of that time.

Reluctantly and slowly, I made my way back to the house. My ears seemed to be singing and my head light. A box of detergent stood on the draining-board in the kitchen and I walked past the dining-room and lounge. At least I could begin to make my bedroom mine again. I stopped on the second tread on the stairs. The lounge door was open. A bowl of soapy water and a scrubbing brush lay by its side, and the pile on the rug stood up as if it were cat's fur, a cat preparing for attack. My brown school shoe lay on its side by the radiogram. The centre light flooded the room. Gordon sat in an armchair in full view of the doorway, a glass of amber liquid in one hand, a cigarette held awkwardly in the other, his eye fixed on the lone shoe. The radiogram was on and 'when I found you gone and love had fled, gone was the dawn, my heart was dead,' Al was lamenting, 'the echo of a song that haunts me ... haunts me ... haunts me ...' The needle had stuck. I could have been on the stair tread for only a matter of seconds before he looked up and saw me. In three strides he came across from where he had been sitting and, ashen-faced, asked how badly I was hurt. He offered me a sip of his drink, whisky or brandy, which made me feel sick again, and put out his hand to touch mine.

'Don't touch me! I hate you, you bastard! I'm going to tell Pauline's dad and her br ... brother Derek an' they'll come here and kill you, they'll kill you, everyone in the market will too!' I screamed. I ran blindly out of the front door into the bitter January afternoon. I ran and ran without stopping in case he decided to follow me in Izzie-Bon or on the motor bike. I knew I was safe once I'd crossed to where the 'plebeians', as his father called them, lived.

Pauline was not at home. A light shone in the front room, but when I knocked and rang the bell, no one answered. Hot from running, I headed slowly towards the town.

I had a sort of picture in my mind, a code known only to me. It comprised various objects and through them I could decipher people and places of safety where I'd stayed in the past. A coal cellar, laurel wreath and toga represented Mr and Mrs Coalman, who'd lived in Roman Road. The buff record sleeves and, what had now to me become a dreaded symbol, a tree signified a family called Buffy. The tree was wood, and stood alongside a patch of grass, thus providing the address: Woodside Green Road. I tried desperately hard to remember the names of the CID officers I'd met in the Lyons Corner House. One was a colour and earth, and the other you kept money in.

I stopped at a telephone box, dialled WHI-1212 and asked for detectives Redditch and Percival. A baffled Scotland Yard telephonist was very patient when I tried to explain where I'd met them and no, I wasn't sure where they were stationed; I thought they all had to report to Scotland Yard at the end of the week or something. Offers of help and a request for the number from which I was dialling threw me into a wild panic, and I replaced the receiver on a very concerned police officer, feeling even more guilty.

Defeated, I made my way back to the Oakeses' house. At what point does the hostage become the hostage-taker? I think it began for me on that bitterly cold January evening. The concern for me from Mrs Oakes was genuine. She'd assumed I'd mopped up the blood-stains from the rug in the lounge, where I must have been 'taken short' so suddenly, and scolded me for cleaning up the sink and everything after I'd been so sick.

She would have done it, I should have left it, I was a naughty girl and she and Dads were about to embark on a search for me. I was imagining Kath or Artie Oakes coming home to find a sink full of vomit and bloodstains all over their lounge rug, not to mention the signs of carnage in the bathroom. I told them I'd been up to Dr Andrews (this was partly true – I'd had to pass his house) and the surgery was so full I decided against waiting.

Mrs Oakes spent the evening putting my room back together after Rosie's long occupation. She vacuumed and polished, cursed Rosie up hill and down dale for the cigarette burns she found and the dirty knickers, stockings, lipsticks and other of Rosie's possessions that were under the bed; moved the furniture around, put a hot-water bottle in the bed for me and brought me up some soup and a junket in a sundae glass. A cup of Horlicks and an Aspro, coupled with this week's *Woman* and *Woman's Own* magazines before she'd even glanced at them herself, gave her a feeling of satisfaction that she'd done all she could for me and more. And she had. She kissed me lightly on the forehead, telling me to 'shout' if I needed anything and that she must go now and minister to Gordon, who, she was certain, had flu and was being naughty by trying to chase it away with brandy. Brandy and milk was acceptable, but Gordon's libations were making him feel dizzy and no one she'd known had got rid of the flu by 'pickling' it!

19

With Mrs Oakes now working happily full time and Mr
Oakes having bought a mate for Mona the myna, whom
he christened Major, Gordon had all the time in the
world to concentrate on his 'love' and to lavish gifts on
me. The first time after that awful January day he
walked sheepishly into the dining-room and laid a flat
paper bag beside one of my exercise books. I reluctantly
looked up at him.

'Open it, Callie, please.'

I obliged, and found a record I'd heard on the radio
many times: 'April Love' by Pat Boone. I can only ever
think of that song as winter and darkness; it certainly
held no promise of spring for me. Perhaps he thought
the lyric about April love being for the very young
would convey the rightness of what had happened.

By the time my fourteenth birthday arrived Gordon
had sold all his Nazi memorabilia, advertising it in *The
London Weekly Advertiser* and *Dalton's Weekly*. I was
amazed by the constant stream of telephone inquiries
about what was available. How many Gordon Oakeses
were there with their Hitler rooms living in Great
Britain?

During one of his many interrogations about my feelings towards him, which he would insist on whenever
we were alone, I had managed to assert that his

adoration of Hitler, the Third Reich and the abomina-
tions that we were now learning about in history was
not conducive to anything that resembled 'love', and
that anyone who collected guns and knives – weapons
that had killed – must be a bit crazy.

'That's it, they've all gone, Callie. You were quite
right. Eh ... I've kept his book though ... eh, *Mein
Kampf*. You don't mind, do you?' He coughed nervously
and danced from one foot to the other, waiting for
my command. When I shrugged my shoulders, he took
that to be an affirmative, gave one of his dazzling smiles
and said 'great', and now how did I feel about him?

'OK, great!' I would repeat parrot fashion. I didn't,
in fact, feel anything for him but a deep-seated anger
and revulsion, and, in a strange way, an obligation,
since I had caused him to do these things. I had knocked
on Hitler's door, and an SS officer had admitted me to
my own concentration camp.

His sickening habits while cleaning his teeth and
during his early morning ablutions also ceased. The
check-list of things I openly despised in him was greatly
diminishing. Even Izzie had been sold and replaced with
a Ford Prefect. Gordon became a true martyr to his
cause, showing me what he would do for 'love' and to
be loved in return, but he might just as well have shared
his room with Adolf Eichmann, bought Izzie a mate –
maybe a Heinkel – and called it Heidi, and blown his
nose and emptied his bowels down the bathroom wash-
basin for all the good it did him. Each night he would
rap three times on the bathroom wall, each rap signal-
ling 'I love you'.

Sometimes, when his parents had been drinking, he
would creep into my room at night. If he was sober, I

could dismiss him with threats of screams. Often, when I would begin to make a sound, panic would ripple through his body and he would hold his hand tightly over my mouth, then back away, his hands held upwards in surrender until he was out of the room. If he had been drinking, there was no escape. I dreaded the door creaking open, my head turned firmly towards the wall – he had long since given up attempting to wrest my head round to face him and had accepted the arms I folded firmly across my chest – the ritualistic prising apart of my stiffened legs, my eyes concentrating on the pale-brown, crinkled shell of the imaginary walnut while the axe-man split the shell asunder, leaving the kernel twisted, bruised and weeping. Of late, the bruising was diminishing, and the ache of being 'tailed' would last for only a day or two.

That summer I gave up my paper round. Deirdre was a secretary in a large department store, and Pauline and I both got jobs in the food department. We would work on restocking the shelves, making pyramids out of canned food and making sure that goods were correctly priced. Sometimes we would work behind the scenes, packaging cooked meats and cheeses in cellophane, carefully wrapping and sealing the goods on a hotplate, which could become extremely hot. There we would weigh and price the products. We didn't often work together and one day, when I was packaging Edam, Danish Blue, Cheshire and various other cheeses, there was an almighty crunch from the shop front.

'Blow-out!' called Jimmy, a lovely old character.

'What's that?' I asked.

The question went unanswered as Pauline was led hobbling and crying into the staff room, where the first-aid kit was kept. Deirdre went rushing by and I was frightened when I noticed the bloodstained trail Pauline had left.

'She's OK, it's not deep, no stitches needed, but you know our Paul – can't stand the sight of blood, specially her own. She's having a hot, strong, sweet cuppa for the shock, and you look like you could do with one too. Titch here can keep Paul company while I ring me dad to take her home, can't she, Jim?' Deirdre had found time to come out to me as soon as she could.

Jim nodded his approval and I went with Deirdre to the staff room, where Pauline was sitting, white as a ghost and with one of her feet bandaged.

'Here's your best buddy to keep you company until Dad comes to take you home, Paul.' Pauline burst into more tears when she saw me. 'Don't be such a baby, Paul. It's the bang frightened you more than anything. It's only a cut about so long.' Deirdre indicated about an inch with her index finger and thumb. 'Drink your tea, come on, and here's yours, Madam.' Deirdre gave me an affectionate pat on the cap we all had to wear when handling food and handed me a cup of tea.

'What's a blow-out, Dee?' I asked, proud to have been invited to share the nickname Deirdre's nearest and dearest bestowed on her.

'It's when a tin blows up. Geoff should have taught you to check for them and he obviously didn't. If you see a tin that isn't flat, looks a bit swollen, like it's got a belly one or both ends, just bring it through and put it in the dumper outside. They don't very often, but some-times, like now, they do explode. The glass jars of deli-cacies, fruits in brandy or some such thing, broke, and my clever sis here cut her ankle, didn't you?'

'I won't again,' Pauline exclaimed.

'That's right, just check your tins. There'll be a full-scale check now, so you'll be dragged away from that handsome hunk Jimmy. Watch him, mind; he's a real ladies' man!'

I laughed at Dee's description of old Jimmy, who looked too old even to be at work, his poor hands all misshapen with arthritis.

'I won't again, Dee, I won't,' Pauline repeated.

'All right, luv, don't start crying again,' Deidre soothed. 'I've got to get back to the office, Paul. Dad won't be that long.'

'I'm not working here any more,' Pauline informed her big sister.

'OK, suit yourself. I'll tell wages. Drink that tea up now then.' Dee left the staff room, eyes raised towards heaven in disgust at how 'soft' her sister was, but there was an indulgent smile on her lips. She'd always spoilt Pauline, and I wished that I had someone like Dee. One thing was for sure: I wouldn't be leaving. I loved working there and I loved the people too, an assorted lot though they were.

'Your brother's waitin', darlin'. Go on. Anybody would think you'd like a bed here. You don't get no overtime or thanks. Go on, off with you,' Kitty, the chief cashier, would say nearly every night.

Gordon had taken to picking me up each evening on the motor bike. How I loathed getting on the back of that bike! I would dream of curling up on the bed in the staff room, with Cherry, one of the girls I'd become friendly with, occupying the sofa. Cherry was younger than me, wore high heels and lots of make-up and even smoked. She was marvellous to work with and had a great sense of humour. Sometimes when we'd had a fit of the giggles over something, we'd go out to a coffee bar on our lunch-break, and she'd tell me about the dances she'd been to and the boys she'd been going out with. Her life seemed so full, and her love of life was infectious. That old familiar flame of guilt would strike at me momentarily when I realized I enjoyed myself much more in Cherry's company than I did in Pauline's.

'Your dad's motor bike's great. I bet it does a ton. Would he let me have a ride on it if you asked? Go on, be a sport,' Cherry begged, her arm looped in mine as we made our way back from lunch.

'My dad?' I asked incredulously. Cherry didn't seem to think this association with the grey-haired man on the motor bike could be anything other than paternal. 'Oh, Cherry, he's not my dad, he's my step-brother. I'm in a foster-home!' I blurted out.

'What, he's got a mum and dad alive? I bet they're old Jimmy's parents and all!' she chortled.

A student named Dave, who was also working at the store during the summer holidays, was Cherry's passion at the moment. He was a very quiet young man and grew deeply embarrassed at Cherry's barely concealed intentions of 'getting him out', as she put it.

'Er, there's a woman here with a query,' Dave informed the Assistant Manager one day while he was instructing Cherry and me on how our time was to be divided.

'She married him, that's her problem!' Cherry retorted, looking at the customer, who was about a foot taller than her husband, and burst out laughing at her own joke. A heavy hand was laid on her shoulder and the Assistant Manager asked her to leave the shop floor and go to his office. He turned his attention to the aggrieved customers, dismissing Dave and me with a wave of his hand.

'She's got a right big mouth, has that 'un. She'll be for cards an' all now.' Dave spoke in a soft Northern brogue. 'I were wonderin', like, there's a right good picture on, *A Summer Place*. Fancy goin'?'

'I'm sorry, Dave, I'm not allowed,' I murmured, more distracted by Cherry's forthcoming sacking than Dave's stumbling words of invitation. At lunch-time I still had not seen Cherry and sadly concluded that she had indeed been dismissed.

'Wotcha!' Cherry said, putting her head around the staff-room door.

Relief washed over me. 'Didn't old Frankie sack you?'

'Course not. Said I was to tone it down a bit and he thinks I'm funny anyway. Put me on helping Deirdre in the office with some filing, but I'm on bacon this afternoon with you. You'll never guess – Dave's asked me to the flicks to see *A Summer Place*.'

A flicker of envy clutched at me and I wished I could have been like Cherry, so carefree, so free! I watched her light a Senior Service, cough and ask for my approval on some stiletto-heeled shoes she'd just bought.

On Sunday morning I announced that the bacon Mrs Oakes had fried for breakfast had probably been sliced by me, as old Jimmy had shown me how to use the bacon slicer the day before. Mrs Oakes looked alarmed. Mr Oakes, noting the pride in my voice at this accomplishment, looked up from the newspaper and asked if it was to be my intended profession. If it were, I thought, I would use him to perfect my art. Thickness-gauge-two slice upon slice of Artie Oakes's flesh would slip from my hand on to the cellophane squares while Jimmy looked on appreciatively at his young apprentice.

Two exciting events occurred that year. The first was Rosie's marriage to her Bill, for which we all made the long journey to a register office in London's East End. Rosie was dressed in a virginal white crocheted dress and coat, and a white hat with a white veil that hung like net curtains over the window of her face. White T-strapped shoes encased her nylon-clad feet, which seemed to be bulging uncharacteristically. Her legs, previously so slim, also seemed to have grown thick, looking more in keeping with her overall frame.

The ceremony was over before I had prepared for it to start, and the twelve or so guests retired to the upstairs room of a pub to partake of the wedding breakfast, as Rosie had insisted on calling it. Bill, a slight man with thinning fair hair, bore a striking resemblance to Stan Laurel. He even scratched his head in a quizzical way and felt the back of his neck as he made his brief speech. I expected him to say 'That's another fine mess you've got me into, Rosie', but instead he praised Rosie, the new Mrs William Dawe, and his good fortune in finding her – an unfortunate choice of phrase, as the late Ada and John had left their only child considerably well off.

Beneath the white crochet beat the tiny heart of Marilyn Ada Dawe, who made her entry into the world within weeks of our return from the nuptial celebrations.

'Just think of her signing her initials in a few years'

time, Paul: M.A.D., poor little thing.' We were in Pauline's room during one of my Sunday afternoon visits. Pauline and I giggled.

'Could have been worse, could have called her Marjorie,' said Derek, looking up from his Western.

'Oh no, Marilyn's much nicer than Marjorie, that's old-fashioned,' Pauline announced.

'He means See-Saw Marjorie Dawe, Paul.' I threw myself back on her bed, laughing uncontrollably.

'Pig!' said Pauline, and threw a hairbrush at him.

'Eh, Paul, when God was dishing out the brains, you thought he said drains and you said, "No, thanks, they stink."'

'And when God was dishing out the chins, you thought he said gins and you said , "Yeah, make mine a double."'

'When he was dishing out the noses, you thought he said roses an' you said, "I'll 'ave the biggest reddest one in the bloody . . ."'

'Cut that out, you two,' Dee said, laughing at their banter. She'd heard it all before and so had I.

'Marjorie Dawe,' I repeated, breaking into fresh giggles.

'Now you've started Titch off,' said Dee. Titch had become my nickname at the department store, and it gave me a great sense of belonging.

The second exciting event that year was Dee's engagement to Derek. One of my favourite records (which I still stole time to listen to on the very rare occasions when I knew that I was completely alone and safe in the house) was 'The Story of a Starry Night'. The night that Dee and Derek got engaged encapsulates those words and brings back the happiest memory I have of my time with the Oakeses.

Mrs Oakes made me a dress in apple-green brocade, and I daringly bought a pair of white sandals with a small heel and lots of straps. I was still working every Friday evening after school and all day on Saturday, and Mrs Oakes came with me during my lunch-break to buy a suitable present. She advised a kitchen clock-timer, which Dee would find, as she put it, 'intervaluable'.

I went with Pauline and her mother to their neighbour, who did our hair. She used to work for the hairdresser Mrs Oakes used, but had worked from home since the birth of her baby. I remember walking out of the house, my hair stiff with lacquer and a gait to match in case a wisp of the hairdresser's creation should stray.

It was a wonderful night. Lots of people asked me to dance and I couldn't believe that the waltz was so easy.

'C'mon, Titch, go with Dad. He'll show you,' Dee persuaded when I protested that I couldn't dance.

'One, two, together. One, two, together. Now I'm the man, I lead. Me Tarzan, you Jane!' Pauline's dad teased.

I was surprised at how easily I adapted to the rhythm of the dances, my confidence increasing by the minute it seemed. I knew many of the tunes that the band played and astounded Pauline's mum and dad with my knowledge of the lyrics.

Dee looked like a film star, with her hair swept up and a corsage pinned to her white dress. The inimitable Derek acted like an innocent bystander in all the celebrations, but when he did make the speech that everyone was calling for, he was, for once, serious. I blinked hard and drank in every word. His speech was brief, but it left a lasting impression. No honeyed words could ever match the love he expressed for Dee that magical night.

Pauline, wearing a powder-blue replica of her sister's dress, her hair swept back in a similar style, did not applaud him. 'He didn't even say she looked nice. He should have written something out and read from it like they do in the pictures,' she complained.

'Oh, Paul, he was lovely ...' I began, before being hauled on to the dance floor by one of her uncles. I realized the gulf between Pauline and myself was wide, but my disappointment in her was fleeting.

'Even though the darkest clouds are in the sky, you mustn't sigh, you mustn't cry, spread a little happiness as you pass by, please try ...' Pauline's dad warbled into the microphone. The song seemed so fitting for Derek and Dee. They did indeed spread a little happiness to everyone, made time for everyone, and each person they spoke to was made to feel the most important person there, as I believe everyone really was to them.

The ballroom had a spotlight, which seemed to be searching for someone. I wondered what I would do if it landed on me, what was expected of me. Happily, it didn't. It was while I was trying to see where the light was coming from that my eyes rested on the ceiling. It was painted dark blue with tiny bulbs scattered, twinkling. It was indeed my starry night.

I was given a glass of champagne to toast the happy couple, but I didn't like it very much and thought I must have been given some fizzy dry cider by mistake.

The band played some Glen Miller and then went into 'The Continental', made famous by Fred Astaire and Ginger Rogers. Pauline's dad took the floor with her mum, his face flushed and his steps either highly skilled and intricate or alcohol-inspired. The spotlight swayed up and down on them, and everyone stood back, laughing and clapping at the look of grim determination on his face and his wife's screams of laughter and fear as, his hand clamped to hers, their arms totally stiff, they strode up and down the floor. We all gasped when he suddenly 'broke' her body in two, leaning her over, his arm clasped under her spine, his feet and hers unsteady. Her head was close to the floor and her 'set' was becoming unset as her hair literally stood on end. Suddenly he pulled her upright. 'B . . . ootiful moozic . . . dangerous rhythm' he sang above the band.

'Too dangerous for me, you daft bugger!' Pauline's mum declared, extricating herself from his grasp. Breathless and laughing, she walked unsteadily back to their table, her face puce.

'More, more, more!' the guests were calling.

'No more for me, darlin', 'cept for another gin an' orange.'

Pauline's mum was frantically fanning herself with her hand, her face looking as if it had been bathed in glycerine, but she was still laughing and I was too. The look of grim determination had never once left her husband's face, even when he'd lost his partner. Now the band struck up 'Top Hat, White Tie and Tails', and, as if on cue, someone threw him a walking stick and he danced a routine with such skill and precision that I was awestruck. I glanced at Pauline while everyone heartily applauded her father, but saw that she looked thoroughly bored.

'Oh, Paul! You didn't tell me, your dad's –' An arm grasped mine and I was pulled to my feet and dragged on to the dance floor before I could finish my sentence.

'There . . . may be ter . . . ubble ahead, but while

230

there's moonlight an' moozic an' luv an' ro ... mance, le's face the music an' dan ... ce!' Pauline's dad was gliding me up and down the floor, his face still deadpan, and I moved along with him, no longer self-conscious and oh so happy. One thing he was right about, there was trouble ahead, but I didn't know, nor would I have believed it on that, my starry night.

20

Mr and Mrs Oakes had gone to 'The Fur and Feather' show. I'd worked on the Friday night at the store and had Saturday off. There was to be a stocktaking on Sunday and I was thrilled not only to have a Saturday off, but also that I was to be paid time-and-a-half for working on Sunday, the one day of the week I had to spend most time in Gordon and his father's company, if I couldn't go to Pauline's for two hours in the afternoon.

I lay in bed that Saturday morning, thinking about the commercial course Pauline and I had embarked on. Pauline, who was faster than I was at typing, just could not grasp shorthand, and I wished I hadn't been so generous in my offer to go to her house to help her and waste a precious Saturday afternoon that could have been spent at the shops. Isaac Pitman was the bane of Pauline's life. 'P', 'B', 'T', 'D', 'CHAY', 'JAY', 'ITH', 'THEE', 'ISH', 'ZHEE' would send her into groans of despair and frustration as we went over the rudiments. 'Ish zheet all right!' she'd once remarked to Dee and me after we'd spent two hours with her. We were due to learn short forms of the language and Pauline seemed to have a mental block. All I could do was console her with her fast typing speeds, but my patience was wearing thin. I wondered if I could ring and say I'd got a sore throat, and then realized I couldn't. I groaned aloud as I concluded I wouldn't be able to get out of it.

'Are you OK, Callie?'

I jumped. I hadn't heard Gordon come in, a mug of coffee in his hand. He had been very aloof and distant since the night I had gone to the engagement party.

'Oh, Gordon, thanks.' I sat up in the bed and took the mug he held out to me.

'Eh . . . have you, I mean, eh . . . did you meet someone at that, eh, party?' He was biting his thumbnail and shifting from one foot to the other.

'What do you mean?' I gathered the sheets round my neck and took a sip of the coffee without looking up.

'Well . . . did you meet some young bloke or . . . eh . . . something?'

'No, Gordon, the only young bloke I had half a dance with was Derek, whose engagement party it was. I did dance with Dee's dad, though, and her uncle, if that's not breaking the law. Why?'

'OK, Callie, OK, don't get mad, I'm sorry. Eh . . . did you enjoy yourself then?'

I nodded, and continued to sip my coffee. I knew he was waiting for me to elaborate, but my starry night was not to be shared with anyone, least of all Gordon Oakes. His hand was outstretched and I looked up.

'I . . . eh . . . don't think you'll get any more out of that.' He pointed to the empty mug that I'd been idly sipping from even though it was empty.

I handed him the mug, thanked him and said I ought to get up. He placed the coffee cup on the dressing table.

'I . . . eh . . . just get worried, that's all . . . you know.'

Suddenly he was kissing my mouth, grasping at my

233

breasts, felling me once more, only more, much more. This time I pushed him to the floor with all my might. The sapling was growing stronger, its branches stronger, stronger from carrying heavy cartons of preserved fruits.

'Don't you ever touch my mouth or these again ever, ever!' I screamed.

He lay on the floor, breathing heavily and mumbling. I turned my face to look at the walnut. The hard, impenetrable shell was opening, cracking at its seams. The rules were there. I hadn't made them, but I'd abided by them. Arthur Oakes had made my 'top' his territory; Gordon had made my 'tail', his. Gordon had for the first time struck for complete control. He had broken the rules.

I heard him zip up his trousers and get to his feet. My head was turned firmly to the wall.

'Oh, Callie, what did I do? I'm sorry, what did I do to make you like that? Oh God, I'm sorry. I knew I'd lose you. You've never been like this. Oh, Christ, what have I done? Please tell me, Callie. Callie, I love you. Please, please look at me, tell me please . . .'

I wasn't going to say anything. The walnut lay in my sights. Pitted, tough and sealed, it wasn't going to crack. Whatever I had done to Arthur and Gordon Oakes to make them divide me in two, neither had the right to cross the boundaries they'd imposed themselves.

'Get out, go away, Gordon!' I hissed.

Silently he obeyed. I heard the door creak open and close. I waited in that bed, damp and cold with my shame. It must have been nearly an hour later that I heard the motor bike's engine start up. I listened until I heard it fade far, far into the distance. I wanted to hear a crash, metal on metal, glass on glass, as Gordon met his father in a head-on collision. Only Mrs Oakes would be in the car too and I didn't want anything to happen to her.

I ran a bath, threw in Dettol and bath salts as a matter of course, and checked the angry red marks beneath the whiteness of my 34A bra. My 'tail' was sore, but my sides had ceased to hurt and I didn't feel bruised. My mouth looked red, but wasn't swollen. I scrubbed myself with the same ferocity as on the other occasions and put on clean clothes. Going downstairs, I made myself a mug of fresh coffee and took it into the darkened lounge, where Mona and Major sat huddled in their cage. I began to shiver. It was November, but it wasn't the coldness of the lounge that turned the shivering into a shaking so violent that I wondered if this was the start of a terrible disease. Coffee spilt on to the surface of the radiogram, and I put the mug down and hurried out to the kitchen to get a cloth. In the hall I reached for my coat and scarf and, donning them, went back into the lounge and sat down until the shaking subsided.

I got up, turned on the orange glow of the radiogram and selected my records. 'Blue moon, you saw me standing alone without a dream in my heart,' the vocalist sang wistfully. 'Black moonlight, where everything reflects your colour, darkness that is endless, nights that leave me friendless.' I needed Ambrose, Roy Fox, Jack Hylton to envelop me in these poignant songs of darkness and despair. 'Looking everywhere, haven't found him yet, he's the big affair, I cannot forget, only man I'll ever think of with regret. I'm gonna add my initial to his monogram, tell me where is the shepherd for this lost lamb? There's a somebody I'm longing to see, I hope that he, turns out to be someone to watch over me,' Jessie Matthews sang the plaintive refrain.

But I didn't want a man to watch over me. The only men I trusted were Pauline's dad and Derek, old Jimmy at the store and the new Assistant Manager, Billy. Frankie had been promoted to Manager.

Billy's wife, Hilary, had worked at the store long before I had and had had one 'holiday', as she called it, to have her fifth baby. She was due for another 'rest' soon, as number six was on its way. I thought for a long time that Hilary didn't like me, but she told me she didn't feel comfy with folk until she'd been around them a long time. 'Hilly' and Billy were known affectionately amongst the staff as the 'Hillbillies'. Billy was far more approachable than Frankie had been, and was popular with customers and staff alike. He used to tell everyone he had chocolate kids: Fry's five boys. He said he was hoping for a sixth boy so that Fry's would have to rename their bars.

'Oh, God, I wish I'd gone in today. I can't stand it here much longer,' I said aloud. The two mynas suddenly began to squawk. 'You two can bloody shut up too!' I shouted at the cage and, putting the last record back, switched off the radiogram and left the room in its cold darkness.

Going into the kitchen I was surprised to find the potatoes, sprouts and carrots prepared. A steak-and-kidney pudding stood in a steamer on the stove too. I rinsed out the mug and went out. Blimp followed me down the garden path and I patted his head, promising him that I'd take him to the park later. Poor Blimp, I was always promising him 'the park', my intentions honourable but unlikely to be fulfilled.

I meandered down to the market. Pauline's mum and dad were busy on their stall, but her mum waved and called out something that I didn't hear. I bought myself some deodorant and a pair of nylons, and then began to buy Christmas presents. I chose the LP of *Kismet* for Mrs Oakes and a bottle of Roman Holiday perfume for Pauline. I saw a boxed salt-and-pepper-pot set that looked like two rosy red apples and was delighted to find I had just enough money left to buy them for Dee and Derek. When I arrived at Pauline's for the dreaded shorthand lesson, she was so fascinated by the perforated pots that she insisted on removing them from their box and filling them with white pepper and salt, which made the base of the box messy. This task gave her the opportunity to dispense with the unwanted shorthand lesson.

The next day I worked all day stocking shelves with Christmas goods. The whole of Sunday was great fun, especially without the prospect of any customers. Afterwards we all sat in the staff room for the first time and Frankie gave us pies and fruit, sweets and even a glass of sherry. Jimmy said sherry was bad for him and that the doctor had 'put him on brandy'. He was more surprised than anyone when Frankie told him to go and get a bottle from the wine and spirits department.

Hilary had spent the day pricing goods, as her baby 'bump', as she called it, wouldn't allow her to do much more than sit now. I was both surprised and hesitant when she asked me if I'd like to come home for a bit of tea and meet the kiddies. I told her I would have to phone and ask.

'You know where the office is, give them a ring,' Billy advised.

Mrs Oakes told me it was most kind of them and of course I could. The staff discount I received on groceries each week made her amenable to any suggestions that the store might make.

The 'Hillbillies'' house threw me right back in time, to a time of my brothers and sister and the noise of a large family. Hilary's mother, a lovely plump lady called Em, looked after the boys while Hilary and Billy worked. I began to visit the family for an hour or so on Sundays after Hilary had left her job to wait for 'Stuart the sixth', the chosen name for her next boy. I'd intended to visit the family on Christmas Eve, but we were so busy that I sent an assortment of cap guns, matchbox cars and painting books via Billy. The whole family had seemed to take a liking to me as much as I had to them. I always left their house feeling sad, though, as the brief flight back to a time when I was part of such a family renewed my sense of incredible loss.

That Christmas found me once again sleeping in the lounge. Mr and Mrs Oakes had taken over my bedroom, while Rosie and Bill and the pretty, fair-haired toddler, Marilyn, had moved into theirs. Rosie, pregnant again, now sat firmly on the settee in the lounge issuing orders to poor 'Stan Laurel', who seemed to enjoy obeying each command. I'd bought the baby a small panda, and Rosie and Bill, a box of chocolates. Mrs Knightley and Mrs Oakes oohed and aahed over this tiny tot, who waddled over with a beam on her face for everyone. She reminded me of my baby sister Anna and I hung back from her as, with annoyance, I felt the tears sting the back of my throat. The child was a delight, even though her mother seemed to spend most of her time admonishing her. But Marilyn, it seemed, had learned to switch off when Rosie addressed her.

'Marilyn Ada, pick that up now, ya little cayer. Sit 'ere, Marilyn Ada. Give Daddy yer shoe, ya little bugger, go on, let 'im put it on, now, this minute.' Marilyn Ada would glance at her mother, scratch her ear, frown and offer her tiny foot to her 'Dadda'.

'She ain't talkin' as much as me mate's little 'un, an 'e's free munfs younger,' Rosie complained.

Over the next few days I learned that Marilyn Ada Dawe's vocabulary was a little more extensive than her mother had given her credit for. 'Duck it', 'Mayindada cayer', 'bugger' and 'chit' were used often by Rosie and Bill's angelic-looking issue.

On my first weekend back at work in January I learned that Hilary and Billy had had a daughter. They'd called her Sandra Hilary Emma, after Sandra Dee, the ecstatic Billy informed me. I bought the baby a pink coat and bonnet with mittens and bootees to match, and Billy drove me to see this delightful new addition to the 'Hillbillies'.

Gordon still rapped out his three knocks on the bathroom wall at night. On his nocturnal visits preceding my birthday in spring he would kiss the side of my cheek as I gazed at that cold, light-brown, puckered walnut shell, then pull the blankets from the bottom of my bed, rolling them up past my waist, and drive deeply into me, whispering words of undying love, and leaving, but not before he methodically replaced the bedclothes, tucked them in and planted a final kiss on my taut, frozen cheek.

*

In June that year a real blow struck me. Some of the boys from school used to call me 'Pekie', because, they said, I had a nose like a Pekinese dog, or 'Sniffer', because I always walked with my head down, eyes firmly fixed on the pavement.

'Oi, stuck up, how d'ya get a nose that stuck up? Try using a 'anky, it might straighten out!'

I could never answer them – I was either too shy or scared – and at first it used to upset me, but eventually I got used to the predictability of their catcalls. If Margaret walked home with me, they would pick on her too. Rob Miller was the leader of the pack and had started the whole thing. One day I had to go to the school secretary and saw Rob sitting outside the Head's office.

'You in trouble too?' he asked.

I shook my head.

Rob took out a comb and started to comb back his hair; I can't recall ever seeing him without a comb in his hand. 'Fancy going to the flicks?'

I shook my head.

'Too good for me, uh?' He leaned his head to one side, raking the comb through his thick blond hair, then repeated the exercise on the other side of his head.

'It's not that, Rob. I'd like to, but I'm not allowed.'

'It's OK, fine. Fine, OK?' He opened both hands, comb still clutched in one, and shrugged in his James Dean manner.

'It has been a great shock to the school and our thoughts and prayers must be for Mr and Mrs Miller, his brother and sister at this tragic time,' the headmaster was saying. I was late for assembly that morning and looked about me only to receive a frown from my English teacher before he bent his head, silently instructing me to do likewise. A minute's silence was to be observed. The first stroke of the piano's chords to 'Crimond' gave me a chance to look about while I sang the hymn. The air was electric, and a silence hitherto unknown to me followed when we were dismissed. Some of the girls were openly weeping, the boys silent, everyone grim.

'Paul, Jill, what's happened?' I caught up with Pauline, who was being supported by Jill and Margaret. All three were crying.

'Rob hanged himself on his bathroom door, Friday night. They said he ... he ... left a note ... afraid he'd fail his O levels.'

I felt as if someone had dealt me a blow to the stomach, and I sucked at the air for breath. 'Rob,' was all I said. How I'd misjudged him. Oh God, how much had this wise-cracking, leader-of-the-pack boy suffered, suffered alone? I went into the toilets and sobs racked my body. I hadn't even known him. He'd only ever spoken seriously to me on that one occasion. What had his last thoughts been? Why couldn't he have told anyone? 'Oh Robin, Robin!' I looked up at the yellowing cracked ceiling of the girls' toilets for an answer and realized I'd spoken his name aloud. 'Who killed Cock Robin?' The thought came unbidden into my head. He couldn't have done it alone. Some other force had driven him to it, a force that I knew only too well.

The following day John William Arthur Dawe was born to Rosie. On the Friday evening Mr and Mrs Oakes were going to the East End for the night to see her and I shuddered at the thought of being left alone with Gordon. Gordon collected me from the store that evening as usual and told me he was nipping over to see his friend Gerry, and did I want to come? I said I was too tired and was still upset over the suicide of Robin Miller. It had been in the newspapers, and there was some talk about a television programme that had shown a hanging and the possibility that Rob could have been experimenting. There was a condemnation from the local MP about the effects television could have on the young. I thought it possible that Robin could have been experimenting, and this gave me some comfort.

I was surprised to awake to brilliant sunshine on the Saturday morning and in plenty of time for the 7.30 bus. Closing the front gate, I saw Gordon's curtains twitch and as I walked up the road, I looked back to see if he would follow me. He didn't, and I felt quite carefree as I alighted from the bus and made my way to the store.

At five o'clock Gordon came into the store to say that his mother had phoned and asked me to get the items on the list he handed to me. I sighed – staff purchases had to be made *before* five – and took the list, and he told me he'd collect me at six o'clock.

I collected the items and took them to Kitty, telling her I'd pay full price, since I hadn't cleared it with Frankie or Billy.

'Don't be daft, luv,' said Kitty as I opened my buff pay-packet. She wrote 'S/D', forged Billy's initials on the till roll and tucked the bag under her seat.

'Ma said to get fish and chips, as they'd be stopping off on the way back for a meal. We'll drop this off, then go for a spin and have a meal ourselves, Callie, eh?'

'It's too hot for fish and chips. Anyway, I'm not hungry. You can tell your mother that I could have got into trouble today for not putting in for staff discount

242

until too late as well,' I grumbled as I got on the motor bike. He started the engine and we roared off down the high street.

'What time did they say they'd be back?' I shouted above the roar of the engine and other traffic.

'After nine,' he shouted back.

It was a quarter past six by the time we got home, which meant I'd be in the house alone with him for three hours if I didn't take him up on his offer, I thought as I put the shopping away, and then remembered, with some surprise, my trouble-free night.

'Well, are you coming for a spin and something to eat? You could just have a banana split or a knicker-bocker glory if you like,' he offered.

'OK. I'll go and get changed.' I went upstairs, washed and changed into a clean dress, cardigan and sandals.

'You'll need something warmer than those togs,' he advised.

'It's still baking hot out there,' I reminded him, and he shrugged as we went out the front door. Reluctantly, I straddled the pillion seat for the second time in forty minutes. I wondered if I could ask him to drop me off at Pauline's house after we'd eaten. Pauline's mum was friendly with Rob's mother and I knew that Pauline's family had taken his death pretty badly. If Gordon could drop me off at Pauline's at eight o'clock and collect me at nine, his parents would be home. I was already beginning to feel cold and I looked over his shoulder for the first time. We were heading in the opposite direction of the town.

'Where are we going, Gordon?' I shouted above the wind. No wonder I was so cold; we were going towards the dual carriageway, where the road widened and there were no houses to shelter us from the wind, and moving at a terrific speed.

'Somewhere special,' he shouted over his shoulder.

'I don't want to go anywhere bloody special, Gordon.' I thumped at the oily leather jacket he wore. Again I banged him on the back. Either he didn't hear me or had decided to ignore me. The ride seemed to go on for ever. Eventually we came off the carriageway and he drove a little more slowly, winding the bike around little country lanes and over a bridge. We turned into a wide road with houses to the left, and grass and hedgerows opposite. Gradually the hedgerows and houses disappeared, and the small stream became a river. We rode on for another ten minutes or so until we were on an incline, then Gordon stopped the bike, parking it near some trees.

'Well, what do you think?'

'I think you're a pig,' I said, repeating Pauline's words for Derek when he made her mad.

'Come on sit down, it's beautiful.' Obediently, I sat on the grassy bank. The sun was dancing on the river and a weeping willow tree bent its branches to drink from the clear, sparkling water.

'If Ma saw this, she'd be singing "old man ribber, dat ole man ribber" by now.'

I was thinking about Robin Miller and how he'd never see the sun again.

'Ma and the old man used to bring me here a lot when I was a kid.'

I didn't respond, but thought about Gordon's mother, who would always be in a world created by Ivor Novello, gathering lilacs in the spring again, or Noël Coward, seeing whoever she imagined she wanted to see again whenever spring broke through again. *Carousel* and *Oklahoma*, *Seven Brides for Seven Brothers*, her world and life lived through musicals. My present of *Kismet* the previous Christmas still found her singing of 'dawn's promising skies, pebbles on a pool drifting'. Something was drifting in a pool now, a water-rat swimming with the most perfect precision I'd ever seen.

'Oh, my God, no, it's a rat!' I went rigid and clutched at Gordon's oily smelling jacket to cover my eyes. Rats belonged to the days of my cat Prowler, my home, my London. Why this sudden terror? This rat was different, his coat wet, fur swept back as if by a wide-toothed comb.

Gordon caught me as I struggled to my feet to run up the bank. Gently, he guided me up and away from the river to where the reeds thinned into shrubs and bushes. Out of breath, I stumbled and Gordon caught me and brought me down on the slope.

'It's OK, Callie, I won't let it hurt you. I'll take care of you, I love you.' Suddenly his mouth closed angrily on mine, he was on top of me, suffocating me. His hand thrust up under my dress, pulling aimlessly, searchingly at my bra, pulling it down, swiftly raking down my petticoat and knickers. My eyes were open in horror, my head unable to escape to the hardness of the walnut. This was the axe-man, no longer felling near the root, but striking through the leaves, splitting the bark wide open. 'Oh, Callie, Callie, I love you, I'm sorry. I've hurt you haven't I? Oh, Christ, Callie, forgive me, I've hurt you. Answer me please, oh Callie, please, say something!'

I stared at blue sky, at wispy clouds of pale pink candyfloss. The sun turned on its rays once more to warm and bring to life the corpse lying on the river bank. The axe-man clothed the young tree, gathering its leaves around it to cover it where it lay, split asunder.

'Callie, darling, please say something, anything, please. I love you.'

He was pulling me, turning me around, pulling me upwards. The lumberjack wanted his quarry just so.

'... *a tree who may in summer wear a nest of robins in her hair ...*' One of the axe-man's mother's songs ... *Trees ... robins ... Who killed Cock Robin? Rats ... Mummy ... Daddy ... Death!*

Someone was laughing, the laughter coming closer, *nearer my God to thee.*

'Oh, Callie, thank God, you're smiling again. What's the joke? Here, let me sort you out. We'll go for fish and chips and a banana split, eh? Come on, it's getting cold, wear my jacket, you're shivering.'

Smooth down the bark, spruce up the leaves, the wind will whip and cleanse you. A banana split – no, it wasn't the fruit that was split. Now sit astride like a split banana and feel the power of the engine surge beneath you. Twist and slide like a sleepy banana. Watch how the axe-man skilfully manipulates the corners, lean to the left, then to the right. A straight run ahead. Feel the power as he accelerates. Less throttle, axe-man, not yet. More acceleration, now slow down with those wrists, those strong wrists. The roundabout is approaching. Lean to your right and – now! The tree has bent its branches deep, axe-man, down, down towards the ground, sparks as the footrest meets the concrete. Everything happens so slowly ... The bike goes up in the air, I fall backwards and the axe-man catapults forwards. The bike's wheels are still spinning and the engine is only purring, but I have taken the power to split the axeman and watch him fall. I wait and watch to see if he will ever rise again. My foot and the back of my head are hurting and I see him getting up, blood on his forehead. Motorists have stopped. Someone has called for someone else to get an ambulance.

'No, no, we're just shaken up. Callie! Callie! Thank God, she's on her feet.'

'But your head, you may need stitches,' a motorist protests.

'No it's only a gash. As long as my sister is all right, and you are, aren't you?'

His sister? His 'sister' reassures the motorist she's fine. The only stitches I wanted for him were an undertaker's

'You tried to kill me! You leaned that bike so far over . . . has it stopped bleeding yet?'

'Unfortunately, yes, yes. Unfortunately I didn't kill you and it has stopped bleeding, stick an Elastoplast over it and tell your precious mummy and daddy you bumped your head, you bastard! Next time I'll get you, that I swear.'

'But, Callie, I love you.'

'Drop dead, you bastard!' I said as I made my way up to the bathroom to cast the usual Dettol and bath salts on the water.

21

During the summer holidays Mrs Oakes confided in me that she was very worried about Gordon. It seemed he was suffering from acute depression and the doctor had prescribed some pills for him. The 'accident' was blamed, and Mrs Oakes felt that Gordon could have delayed concussion. I too was suffering from depression, not only because of the accident or the incident that preceded it, but also because the inquest on Rob Miller had confirmed that he had left a suicide note and the verdict was that he had committed suicide while the balance of his mind was disturbed. This phrase seemed bizarre to me, as it was only with the utmost clarity and intent that I had tried to end my life. I brooded as I thought of my hands holding the bottle of aspirin and Rob's holding the rope.

Pauline returned to work at the store that summer. One Saturday night her mum and dad, Dee and Derek decided to go to see a show. Pauline asked if I could stay the night with her, as they wouldn't get home until late. I asked Pauline if she could get her mum to telephone the Oakeses for permission.

When Kathleen Oakes walked into the dining-room I was sure that permission had not been granted. The atmosphere hung over the room as comfortless as a naked 25-watt bulb.

'You know who that was and her reason for telephoning me?' Her lips were set as they were when she took her first drink of sherry, her voice stilted. I waited in silence, inwardly cringing, not wanting to hear what she'd told Pauline's mum. 'I said you could go as long as it wasn't going to be halibutal. You knew she was going to phone me, didn't you, but you kept me in the dark, making me look a fool in front of market people, didn't you?'

I nodded and, knowing better than to say I was sorry, thanked her very much.

'Have a bath when you come back, mind, on Sunday. People like that top and tail their sheets once a month, you know.' She sniffed and walked out of the room.

Well, there won't be the need for casting Dettol and bath salts on to the water, Mrs Oakes, and 'your men' know all about topping and tailing. How clean the blue-packaged starched sheets and pillowcases come back from the Sunblest Laundry you send them to. Is there a Fleshbest Laundry you could send my body to, Mrs Oakes, that could ever cleanse me? I think not, Mrs Oakes, I think not.

Pauline and I left the store that Saturday night in a state of high excitement, and Derek drove us with Dee to Pauline's house.

'Glad your foster-mother let you stay as long as you keep off the halibutoil,' Derek said as we all trooped into their living-room. I saw Pauline's mum give him a warning look and he clapped his hand over his mouth.

'It's OK, she always gets her words wrong,' I said, laughing at her latest malapropism. She'd repeated it often enough over the past two days. Pauline told me her mother had said Mrs Oakes was a toffee-nosed bitch and not a very bright one at that. I'd felt slightly defensive about Mrs Oakes when Pauline had told me that, but I didn't feel that way now. In fact, in a perverse way, I even wanted to relate some of her sayings to entertain them, and maybe I would have if they hadn't all scattered to get ready.

Once they had gone – Pauline's mother's instructions to tap on the wall to the neighbours if we were nervous still ringing in our ears while we waved enthusiastically until their car turned the corner – we got down to the serious business of enjoying ourselves. Pauline's dad had left us two bottles of Babycham each, and crisps and nuts and bars of chocolate. We spent the evening with the record-player turned up full blast as we devised new rock-and-roll steps to Presley's 'Hound Dog' and Jimmy James's 'Good Timin'' amongst many others. A ring on the doorbell made us both jump. It was loud and persistent. It was one of the Oakeses; I knew I wouldn't taste such fun and freedom for long. With the awful prospect of seeing Gordon's face, I followed Pauline to open the door.

'Mind turnin' the music down, our Paul? Only we can't 'ear the telly properly, luv.'

'Sorry, Auntie Peg,' said Pauline, reassuring the tall middle-aged, red-headed woman who stood on the doorstep smiling woodenly at us.

'We did tap on the wall, but you couldn't have heard us, luv.'

Once again Pauline apologized, but as soon as we got into the living-room we burst into fits of giggles over who had tapped on whose wall.

'Will she tell your mum?' I asked, suddenly realizing there could be far-reaching consequences, consequences that could reach the Oakeses if Pauline's mum got angry and there was trouble.

'No, otherwise I'd have to tell her husband.'

'What do you mean?'

'I'd have to tell him we disturbed his missus and her feller from watching telly while he was away for a month with his firm.'

'Oh, Paul, what a thing to say!' I was genuinely shocked.

'No, everyone knows about Peg and her husband, who's a traveller. Her bloke's a traveller too: he travels over here every time her husband goes away. Travels all over her too! She looks well travelled, doesn't she?' We both broke into fits of uncontrollable giggles.

We made up each other's faces and painted each other's toenails crimson. At eleven o'clock we went to bed and exchanged stories about what Peg and her boyfriend, Fred, would be doing, and imagined what Rosie and Stan, as Pauline always called Bill, would be doing. Our swear-word, borrowed from little Marilyn's vocabulary, was 'Duck it'.

'Sh . . . sh . . .' Pauline hissed.

Suddenly I was scared, hearing an unmistakable noise coming from downstairs. I stiffened, wildly imagining Gordon creeping up to our room.

'Duck it, they're back,' Pauline hissed.

The luminous hands on the clock read 1.30. A long sigh hissed from my mouth and I realized I'd been holding my breath. I could hear Dee giggling. A few moments later, on Pauline's instructions, I pretended to be asleep when her parents put their heads around the door.

'Bless 'em,' her mum said and closed the door again.

Pauline and I were still trying to muffle our giggles an hour later. The night seemed endless and my ribs ached with laughter.

'There you are then, you two. Did you sleep well? Tea's in the pot, Paul. Want some toast?' Pauline's mother looked over the top of the *Sunday Pictorial* she was reading at the kitchen table and, smiling, hooked a chair out for me with her foot. 'You were dead to the world when we came in. Did you have a nice evening?'

Pauline, who sat beside me, said airily that it had been great and there'd been no need to tap next door, which brought on another giggling fit.

'What's up with you, you soppy date? What's tickled her?' Pauline's mother asked me, which caused me to join Pauline in her giggles.

'Did you all have a good time?' I inquired when I'd regained my self-control.

Pauline's mother spread thick slices of cold toast with butter and honey, cut them up into four small squares and handed us each a plate. She poured two cups of tea, stirred in the sugar and passed them to us. All this she did effortlessly while remaining seated in her chair. I swallowed hard, feeling my throat constrict as I looked at this lovely woman who thought it the most natural thing in the world to cut up our toast. I'm sure if there had been boiled eggs she would have made us 'soldiers'.

'Oh, it was marvellous. That Max Wall, well, I've heard the expression "rolling in the aisles" but I never thought it really happened. He had on these boots, oh my God, and these yellow tights on his little stick legs . . .' She went on to describe Max Wall's antics and said, 'It was a shame some of his jokes were a bit, well, you know, not suitable for you girls, otherwise we'd have taken you. He's near the bone, mark you.' As she spoke she was cutting more squares of toast and honey.

'You going to church tonight, Mum?' Pauline asked.

'Paul, when do I miss church, especially now? Ellen Miller's coming, God love her. I hope we can bring her some comfort.'

'Do you go to St Peter's?' I asked, surprised that Pauline's mother was a church-goer, although I realized that my Sunday visits ended before an evening service would begin.

'No, my love, I belong to the Spiritualist Church, and very proud I am too.'

'Mum's a medium,' said Pauline nonchalantly, munching her toast.

'Does that mean you get in touch with the dead?' I asked, awash with fear.

'I do have that gift that I'm blessed with, to help us on this side get in touch with those who have passed on to the other side, as we call it. As naturally as we are here now, we all pass over into the spirit world, but there's nothing to fear, it's just as natural to be over there.'

'Does that mean that you can speak to Rob ... tonight?' My voice was barely a whisper and my fingers were trembling as I gripped the teacup tightly in both hands.

'Maybe, maybe not. You can't always get through. Sometimes there are so many guides wanting to come through that I don't always get to the people who most need me, like poor Ellen. You see, nothing is final. We all go round and round in a circle like the world does. Look at this summer. In a couple of months it will be gone, the flowers will have died and the leaves will fall off the trees, but in spring they'll come again.' Her hand went around my shoulder as she went on to explain that her Church worked with God and Jesus, and didn't he come back to show there was life after this life? I knew she could feel my body trembling.

'Are Dee and Derek spiritualists?' I asked feebly.

'Yes, of course they are, darling; we all are. Now there's nothing to fear with Dee and Derek or our Paul or our Dad, is there? Not that they're mediums. It's a rare gift that's God-given. Each and every one of us has our spirit guides, as we call them. You've got two, did you know that?'

'Two what?'

'Guides. I could tell you things about yourself. You have two Sisters-of-Mercy who I've often seen standing behind you.'

The familiar throb of fear began its tattoo at the base of my spine and I wanted to run away from this house and these people I had come to love so much. Perhaps this was the real reason Mrs Oakes didn't want me to stay at Pauline's.

'Listen, you've nothing to fear. Your guides are with you all the time.' I was thinking that there was never a happy ending, that my two Sisters-of-Mercy hadn't done a very good job in protecting me so far, but instead I tried to clear my throat, which had constricted, hampering my swallowing.

'Listen, darling, I know your mum and dad are "in spirit", but they're happy now.'

'Have you seen them? Have you talked to them?' My voice was a whisper.

'Oh well, I ... er ... haven't spoken to them, no.

Listen, there is nothing to fear from the spirit world. All your mummy and daddy want is for you to be happy. I could try to get in touch with them, if you want me to. If you stay another time, I'll try to bring them to you. It isn't frightening, there's no lights out and candles burning like you see on soppy pictures, you know. I do it here at this very table, don't I, Paul?'

Pauline agreed with her mother, and I felt badly betrayed. Why had Pauline never told me her family were spiritualists? Fear still beat at my spine as I wondered if my father had revealed my part in my mother's death to Pauline's mother. Oh God, no, the thought suddenly struck me, what if he had? What if it were common knowledge in Pauline's household?

'Have another cuppa, darling, and don't look so afraid. It's as natural as breathing.'

Breathing was the last thing I was able to cope with naturally at the moment.

'Mum can levitate things too. You know the big oak sideboard? I've seen Mum make that thing move two feet in the air by itself. Ask Dee and Derek; they've seen her do it as well,' Pauline announced proudly.

I didn't know what levitate meant, but asked if the spirit world could make her move furniture and wondered why. Once again her arm went round my shoulders and she assured me that it was another gift to prove the existence of the world of spirit to those who doubted it.

... and so it was that Snow White took pity on the poor pedlar, never believing her to be the Wicked Witch, and bought the shiny red apple ... and taking the delicious-looking toast thickly spread with honey, she bit into it and fell as if in death.

I ran across the park after agreeing with Pauline and her mother that I would spend another night with them again very soon. I raced up the garden path and was relieved to find no one at home. I ran a bath and cast my usual offering of Dettol and bath salts on to the water. Grief and a sense of loss overcame me, and I cried until the bathwater was cold. My eyes were still puffy when the Oakeses came back from having sherry with the Knightleys.

'Up all night by the looks of you,' Mrs Oakes snorted with a degree of satisfaction. I wondered fleetingly who her guides were and shivered.

The pressure of schoolwork was heavy on us now and I saw Miss Crowley only every six or eight weeks, so it came as a surprise to me when I arrived home one day to find a note saying that a new officer would be calling to see me on Tuesday at 4.30 p.m. If this was inconvenient, she would be grateful if I could telephone her at the number above. It was signed 'J. Cox'. I wondered what had happened to the old Crow.

I could hardly believe my eyes, that Tuesday in late October, when I opened the door to a petite, dark-haired lady, who looked young enough to be Miss Crowley's granddaughter.

'Hi, I'm Jane, Jane Cox,' she introduced herself, holding out a hand even smaller than my own. 'May I come in? You did get my note, didn't you, Caroline? It is Caroline, isn't it?'

'Yes, yes, of course, I'm sorry I . . .'

She must have seen how startled I was by her age compared with that of her predecessor. 'This way? Think I look a bit young for the job, eh?' she asked.

'Yes, go through.' I escorted her into the dining-room,

where the winter curtains guarded the french doors. I made us both some coffee. As soon as I'd sat down she asked if she could have an ashtray, and astonished me by offering me a cigarette. I said I didn't smoke, and she replied that lots of people did at my age. From the very start of our relationship she treated me as a friend and an equal. She was interested in my schoolwork and my clothes, and asked to see my bedroom, which she thought really pretty. She asked how everyone was in the house. How, she inquired, was I managing to come to terms with the loss of my family? Her questions seemed endless; her knowledge of the Top Twenty and what was going to be 'in' this winter staggered me. I found her both exhilarating and exhausting.

I had always been able to predict Miss Crowley's questions, which had never varied, except when I'd run away. She would drink her cup of tea and look at her watch as she rose to go. It seemed Miss Crowley was sick and would not return to work, having decided on early retirement.

It was with relief, tinged with disappointment, that I let Miss Jane Cox out of the house, having been instructed to call her Jane too. It was with even greater astonishment that I realized I'd shown her my mother's pink scarf, lock of hair and my Mabel Lucie Attwell Annual. She had amazed me by saying that these were important things for me to keep.

Later that evening she telephoned and asked if she could visit the Oakeses. It was decided that she call at 6.30 p.m. on Friday.

'But I'll be at work,' I protested.

'I think that's the general idea,' Artie Oakes murmured, looking up from his newspaper.

Gordon didn't tap out his message very often now, and on the odd occasion that he did, I would find myself taut and shaking. He came into my room only when he'd been drinking. Mr and Mrs Oakes had bought themselves a new, large, four-door saloon car to accommodate Mona and Major's cage, as they would sometimes show the birds. Breeding boxes had been purchased, vets consulted, but so far Mona had failed to produce any minor mynas for the Oakeses.

It was in early November that Jane sprang a surprise question as we sat sipping coffee in the dining-room: 'Caroline, are you happy here?' The question was thrown out casually as she inhaled on her cigarette, and a look of surprise must have registered on my face. No one had ever asked me that before. All I could remember was being told that I could get worse placements. The directness of the question, quite apart from the question itself, threw me off guard.

'Um ... yes. I mean, I'm doing my O levels, I've got lots of clothes Mrs Oakes makes me. It's a lovely house, isn't it? Pauline's my best friend at school [*don't dwell on your self-imposed estrangement from Pauline*], then there's the garden and ...'

'You still haven't answered my question. Are you happy here?'

'Yes, of course, I've been here a long time now. Then there's the store, that's really fantastic, the people there are really marvellous!' I enthused.

'Are you working there over the Christmas holidays?'

'Yes. Why? Aren't I allowed?' Dismay nearly overwhelmed me.

'Of course you are, but after Christmas I'd just do Saturdays if I were you. These exams coming up are going to take a lot of concentration, and weighing out people's potatoes or whatever –'

'Oh, I don't weigh potatoes,' I interrupted her.

'Well, whatever. Look, here's my number at home as well as work. If you ever need me, I want you to ring me, even if it's for a silly chat. I'm the expert at silly chat or so my boyfriend tells me.' She took my hand in hers and squeezed it.

I deeply resented that she could advise me – or was it warn me? – that I might have to reduce my time at the store, where I was so happy, and reluctantly took the card on which she had written a phone number marked 'home'.

That Christmas was the first one I'd spent at the Oakeses without Rosie. The house was as silent as the grave. Even Mr Knightley was on duty on Christmas Eve and Mrs Knightley arrived alone.

I realized on Christmas night that however bad Rosie had been, she'd brought some life into this house. Mrs Oakes turned the volume up full on the radiogram as if to compensate for the lack of laughter and the presence of the ghosts of yesterday.

On Boxing Day Gordon stayed in bed all day and his mother took trays up to his room.

'He's getting more and more of these heads now, Artie. D'you think we should get him to see a specialist?' Kathleen Oakes looked genuinely concerned for her son; Dr Andrews had not convinced her it was migraine.

'Ask Andrews to recommend one if you're worried, Kath.' Arthur Oakes didn't look up from his Christmas present, a book on whose glossy cover a bird's wings spanned the spine.

Mr and Mrs Knightley were coming this evening. At least that would be some different company. I would have gone to see the 'Hillbillies' if they hadn't lived so far away, but there weren't any buses running. Oh God, I wished Pauline's mum hadn't revealed the 'gifts' she was blessed with. I would have gone there, but I couldn't face the messages I'd received from the living over the past few years, never mind the dead!

I went to bed that night thoroughly depressed, feeling guilty about not seeing Pauline and her family and missing them, although I'd sent them all presents through a tight-lipped Pauline. I also felt guilty that Gordon suffered from these 'heads' and depression. I'd been asleep for some time when I awoke because my feet and legs were freezing. I kicked around, searching for the blankets and eiderdown to cover myself. There was a heavy bundle lying across my chest.

There was no perfunctory kiss on the side of the frozen face, just the hard, hot, urgent thrust, painful enough to make me cry out. I turned my face to the 'walnut' in the dark; the axe-man had struck. No longer were words of love used, nor forgiveness begged. He completed his task and crept away like a thief in the night.

I lay as he had left me, cold and exposed. The ritual of tucking me in had gone as swiftly as he had, and I lay there wanting the physical pain of the icy temperature to numb me. The damp warmth of my shame turned to ice on the sheet beneath me and still I did not move. I lay crying warm tears, a warmth that could not melt the ice. Hot, hot cheeks, cold, cold body of shame.

Eventually I swung my legs over the bed. Paralysis from the cold made me stagger like a toddler taking its first steps. I sat back on the bed.

Bomp! Upsadaisy. C'mon again. Good girl, clever girl.
And again. There she is. Steady now, up we get.

Drunkenly, I made my way to the bathroom and
cleansed myself. I was surprised to find that, though my
sides were aching and I was sore, I didn't feel bruised.

The following night they all got very drunk and I
waited with the bedside lamp on. I didn't see Gordon
that night or the following day.

I was relieved to return to school in January. A chart
had been pinned up in the Commerce Room showing
the names of all the students and the words per minute
each had attained in both shorthand and typing. I was
ahead of the class by fifteen words per minute in shorthand and ten behind in typing. I was pleased to see that
Pauline was second in typing speeds.

Collecting my wages one Saturday night from the
office, I found Dee's arm on my shoulder. She asked if I
could spare a few moments. I thought Jane Cox must
have phoned to say I had to cut down on my hours in
the store, and frowned at the prospect, but waited.

Cherry, who had left the store some time previously,
had returned now. Kitty said she'd 'got into trouble'
and had had to go away and that her baby had been
adopted. I hadn't believed Kitty, but Cherry had certainly changed, and I wondered now, as she meekly
asked for her wages, whether the rumour was true. With
Cherry gone, Dee asked me to sit down, and I did so
reluctantly.

'You and Paul broken friends, luv?'

'No, it's just that I'm not allowed to stay at people's
houses the night any more,' I lied.

'Um ... did Mum mentioning being a medium have anything to do with your not being allowed to come?'

'Oh no, I didn't tell them about that!'

'Did Mum's talk scare you?'

'No,' I lied emphatically.

'Listen, shall I tell you something? You listen now. Mum has got a certain gift, as she calls it; don't ask me where it comes from. Mum's a good woman and her Church and her gift are part of her life. I used to go with her to the Spiritualist Church and believe in it all when I was Paul's age. She even had Derek going there for a while and Dad goes occasionally too.'

'Does that mean you're not all Spiritualists?'

'No, but you know our Mum. If we told her we weren't, not that she ever assumes anything other than that we are, it would hurt her and so we ... we just go along with it. Mum wouldn't harm a fly. Like I say, she's a good woman and it's her belief and it's Paul's ... at the moment. Mum's been worried sick that that was what had upset you, especially with your mum and dad, well, you know ... oh, come here .'

Dee put her arms around me and rocked me gently. I began to cry and when at last she released me I saw her face was tear-drenched too.

'We'd better share this, soppy date, as Mum would say.' She proffered a tiny white lace handkerchief. 'Here, ladies first, angels after.' She took the handkerchief to wipe her eyes and made me promise to come around to see the family on Sunday.

I said perhaps the Sunday after, as I'd feel awkward walking back into the house without making it up with Pauline first.

Cherry was waiting for me as I left the store. It was bitingly cold.

'Been crying? Haven't got the sack, have you?'

'No, I've got a cold that's all.'

'Oh yeah? Well, pull the other one. Is your half-brother giving you a lift on his motor bike? If not, my dad should be here soon, he'll drop you off. I'm not allowed to buy a Mars bar without my dad being there, thinks there might be a man from Mars who'll make me have another little martian. Here he is now. Come on get in.'

So it was true. Cherry did have a baby. Her joke about the martian was thrown out with bitterness. The Cherry so full of life and laughter had gone.

22

My renewed friendship with Pauline and the warmth of the welcome back I'd received from the entire family lifted my spirits, and the terrible void that being away from them had created was filled. There was never again even a mention of any other form of 'spirit'. Plans were being made now for Dee and Derek's wedding in September, and my joy when Dee said she wanted me as a bridesmaid made me feel as if yeast were rising within my very being, lightening my footsteps and lifting my thoughts to dizzying heights.

Once again Pauline's family asked me to go out with them. It was to a St Valentine's Day dance at the ballroom of my 'starry night'. Mrs Oakes had said 'that's nice' about the honour bestowed on me by being chosen as Dee's bridesmaid, and only added with some acerbity that she assumed the dresses would be 'shop bought'. Although I had confirmed her assumption, she had raised no objection. It was a surprise to me, therefore, that she refused to allow me to go to the St Valentine's Day dance because the Knightleys were coming to dinner. She left me in a cold fury and I even cried bitterly in front of Pauline.

'Tell the old cow you're not staying the night then; tell her Derek and Dee will bring you home. Dad'll come and collect you after you've had dinner with Bert the Bobby and his wife. Come on, she can't say no to that surely.' Pauline was pleased with her advice on the course of action to be taken, and, seeing the sense of this compromise, I ran home to tell Mrs Oakes.

Unlike the 'gal who cain't say no', which she'd sung often enough through the years, she proved that evening she could indeed say no and added that she 'didn't mean maybe'!

On St Valentine's Day Gordon handed me a white box as I was coming out of the bathroom. I hadn't had any more visits from him since the 'night of ice', as I came to think of it. I took the box without even thanking him and, going into my bedroom, I waited until I heard him shut the bathroom door before I sat on the bed and opened it. On the card bulged a large satin ruby-red heart with the words 'To My Sweetheart' written in a garish blue script. Inside words of endearment penned by a writer of romantic valentine verse were joined by Gordon's protestations of undying love.

Mrs Oakes had taken the afternoon off and I came home to the smell of roasting chicken. Two bottles of white wine stood outside the back door to chill. She was singing 'Everything's in Rhythm with My Heart' and beamed at me as I walked into the kitchen. I couldn't bring myself to even look at her as I went up to my bedroom. I could hear her accompanying Jessie Matthews in the verse of the song and, throwing myself on the bed in despair, felt the sharp corner of Gordon's boxed card, which I'd pushed under my pillow that morning. Well, the Oakeses had a good verse for to-night: 'Caroline, she took an axe and gave fosty-mummy forty whacks. When she saw what she had done, she gave the woodmen forty-one.'

'First wedding anniversary we've spent together for years, and the meal was lovely, Kath, it really was.' I hadn't known it was the Knightleys' wedding anniversary that had caused me to be placed under 'house arrest'. I dived into the washing-up with gusto, after having been kissed by both Knightleys for the enormous heart-shaped box of chocolates I'd known nothing about and accepting their thanks as graciously as I could.

The lounge had been opened up like one of the stately homes of England, and a fire burned in the grate.

'Leave the wiping-up, ducks, I'll do that. Come and drink a toast to Marion and Bert. It's their "Silver", you know.'

I didn't know what a 'Silver' was and assumed it to be something not quite up to an Olympic gold, if this was how marriages were graded.

Kathleen Oakes, flushed with wine, put Frank Sinatra on the radiogram, telling everyone to 'hush', which we did. We listened for a while to what sounded like Frankie clicking arthritic bones before he began to sing 'My Funny Valentine': 'Is your figure less than Greek?' 'ol' blue eyes' asked.

'Is your figure less than greet?' Kathleen Oakes's voice rose above Sinatra's.

'Not "greet", Ma; it's "Greek"!' Gordon told her, sipping his drink.

'It's "greet", Gordon, "greet". It's the way the Americans talk. I should know.'

'Ma, how can anyone have a figure tha's less than "greet", for God's sake?' Gordon demanded, his voice slurred.

''Cos, Gordon, "great" wouldn't rhyme, an' anyways,

who'd want a figure that was less than Greek? All Greek women turn to fat early, you know,' Mrs Oakes announced triumphantly.

I stayed to watch the Knightleys unwrap the silver tray that had been bought for them, and accepted further kisses for something I'd known nothing about. Still the rage inside me burned as I thought of missing another 'starry night' and listened to the Oakeses' plans for the two new myna birds that would be arriving in a few weeks and how they and the Knightleys should seriously start thinking about the wine-making they were going to embark on this year. I found my voice growling a 'goodnight and happy silver'. None of them seemed to notice the hobby of yesteryear make an exit.

I climbed the stairs to face *The Merchant of Venice* and *Silas Marner*, but neither the Bard nor George Eliot could hold my attention. Again and again my thoughts wandered to the ceiling of a thousand twinkling stars under which Pauline's dad would be dancing 'The Continental'. Echoes of that one night of magic ... what was that song? 'Begin the Beguine', that was it. The weight of self-pity sent my head slapping against the textbooks, and I buried my face in Portia's tale and wept.

'I can't dance, Ma. Oh, come on, Ma!' I could hear Gordon's voice choking with laughter, which turned into giggles, and a not unpleasant, melodic boom, boom, boom from the radiogram drifted upwards to penetrate the walls. What was Elizabeth Barrett Browning's 'Sonnet to the Portuguese'? Something about thanking someone who stopped outside her prison walls to hear her music. I cocooned myself within the soft prison walls of the eiderdown, trying to recall the sonnet.

'Did ... did ya like the car ... card, Callie? Issa 'cos I love ya, Callie ... Callie, c'mon ... I love ya ...' Gordon's voice thick in my ear, the smell of whisky on his breath.

I turned my face to the wall. My cheek fell upon cold hardness, a page of the textbook on my pillow. My body rigid, I drew my left arm tight across my breasts.

'Iss OK, I'm not gonna touch your top half. See, I love you, Callie, I wouldn't hurt your top half.'

I waited for the cold air to assault my legs. I hadn't undressed and he dragged my pants down past my stockings. I waited for what seemed an age before the familiar weight drew itself upon me. Keep looking at the walnut, cheek pressed on to hard paper, trees, paper came from trees just as the walnut did, tree, paper, walnut ... the sooner the axe struck, the swifter would the heavy earth burying you lighten; the tree's roots would grow strong again, hard wood, hard unyielding walnut, paper softening, warming ... the walnut, don't lose sight of the walnut. Why this waiting, fumbling, laboured breathing, my breathing labouring under this weight? The axe was not striking. Fingers were probing my inner thighs ... look at the walnut, the tree ... the axe-man was trying to drive a soft, sun-warmed plum into me, its velvety smoothness refusing to bruise its own soft, warm flesh against mine. Tomorrow came and went as I lay rigid. The weight suddenly lifted, fell away, air rushed at my exposed flesh and I, hungry for the sharp intake of cold air to assail my lungs, felt an overwhelming sense of gratitude.

He was not going to cover me. I heard his breath coming in deep gasps from above my head.

'Look at what's 'appened, Callie. I can't even do it. I

can't, an' iss your fucking fault, Callie, you made me
... I didn' wanna love you an' now look what you've
made me ...' An ugly sob rasped from his throat as he
opened the bedroom door without his usual stealth. I
heard him stumble once and then his bedroom door
open and close. I had never heard Gordon swear before
and, in a strange way, that fact and the very strangeness
of the event struck as much terror into me as the night
the axe had first felled me.

He'd said that I had made him. Oh God, what had I
made him do? What had I made his father do too? Why
had I made them do it? I'd hated it when they hadn't
liked me and had ignored me, and when I'd tried to
make them like me, I'd hated that even more. They had
'topped' and 'tailed' me. As I covered my legs, a tremor
began to shake my body, and seemed to go on for ever.
Even when it subsided, I found that I couldn't cry. My
throat felt as if a heavy yoke weighed on it, and I
couldn't make a sound. I got up and washed and put on
my nightclothes. I cleaned my teeth and eventually
managed to swallow some of the frothy mint to de-
anaesthetize my throat. I had spent many unhappy days
and nights at this house, but this, this St Valentine's Day
Massacre, was one of the worst.

I'd ask Jane Cox. I'd phone her office tomorrow and
tell her that I'd go wherever they put me. The candle
flared as I wondered what secret her buff-coloured file
on me contained, and decided that whatever it said
about my mother would be added to by what I had
caused to happen here. I now knew I could face isolation
and any punishment 'they' saw fit to give.

I took the card Jane had given me and telephoned her
office from the red box opposite the school. I was told

she was on a day's leave. I telephoned her home number and let the phone ring and ring. I clutched the heavy black receiver while I watched the usual late stragglers going through the school gate. I counted up to fifty and put the phone down in defeat. I walked into school, deciding that I wasn't going to sit my examinations and I certainly wasn't going to rely on Jane bloody Cox ever again. I didn't even want to see her again. I could leave school and get a room. Some of the others had left already. I could get a job in a hairdresser's or even maybe as an office junior. Decision made, I walked with slow deliberation into the classroom and smiled as I was informed I'd got a late mark.

I sailed through that day in a dream, and after dinner that night, while the Oakeses were fussing about with Mona and Major, I took the local evening paper up to my room. There were plenty of jobs available, office jobs too. There were also bed-sits, but they were all near here. I knew that if I were ever to escape I would need to lose myself in a big city. I remembered that Mr Taylor sometimes used to order London or Manchester or Birmingham papers for some of his customers. I looked at the clock; it was too late. I would order some papers in the morning and go where no one would ever fine me again.

I awoke during the night, a pressure on my stomach. I automatically turned my face to the wall. I couldn't hear him breathing and when I released my own breath, the intensity of pain in my abdomen made me gasp. I sat up and lay down again swiftly. I was alone and helpless in my pain. If I called for help, the axe-man might come and help himself. Gingerly, I shifted myself slightly on to my side to find a more comfortable position. I was perspiring now and suddenly nausea swept over me. I got out of bed clutching at the pain, holding it as if it were a tennis ball of fire in my stomach and I could contain its spread by gripping it. Bile ran through my fingers as I ran into the bathroom and, just in time, vomited violently into the toilet bowl. I sat with my knees bent double, clutching the fire-ball until the retching subsided. When the pain lessened, I struggled to my feet. I crept back into the bedroom, my mouth sour, poisoned. Memories of Frederick Seddons' house in Tollington Park returned. Hadn't he poisoned his lodger? What was I other than Eliza Mary Barrow to Frederick Seddons alias Gordon Oakes? I was a lodger in his house too. I switched on the bedside lamp, fear spicing my brain, along with the pain in my stomach and the heat of my body. I lay with just the top sheet covering me and felt my stomach. It was swollen tight. I rolled the sheet down to look for any signs, but there were none, just the sheen of my hard, taut belly.

Towards dawn I drifted off to sleep. Now and again I woke and tried to push the irritation away with the heel of my hand. Suddenly I awoke and ran to the bathroom and was violently sick again. I'd nearly collided with Arthur Oakes, who yelled 'Hey, just a minute, gurl!' before I slammed the door shut in his face. I lay on the floor, my cheek resting against the cold white porcelain of the toilet bowl, vaguely aware that there was a commotion going on outside the bathroom door. Mrs Oakes was rapping her knuckles on the door and I rose to my feet. I flushed the toilet, then slowly went to the basin and washed my face and cleaned my teeth. I let the water gush and swirl around the basin before silencing its flow with great deliberation.

'Open this door, ducks. C'mon, we all want to go, you know. Listen, Dads and our Gordon will break it down if you don't come out! I know you're in there,' she called with remarkable perception.

I emerged from the bathroom, my hands across my stomach, guarding myself against the assault from within, as so often, arms across my breasts, I'd guarded myself against the assault from without.

'Oh my God, get Andrews, Artie, get Andrews!' Her arms around me, Mrs Oakes escorted me back to bed and tucked me in, only to throw back the sheets again for me to show her where the pain was.

'How long you been like this, eh? All night?'

I could only nod.

'How long's your belly been out like this, eh? Artie, get your white shirt on and phone Andrews this minute. I can't have him seeing these sheets like this. I'll have to get some clean ones. Hang on there, luvvy.' She went to the bathroom and came back with fresh bedlinen.

Dr Andrews arrived just as Kathleen Oakes was removing the last tinny curler from her head. He was a big white-haired man and I winced as he sat on the side of my bed, his bulk shifting the position of my painful abdomen. He took my temperature and pulse. I kept my eyes on his face, which registered nothing to indicate alarm.

'Now then, pop the clothes back and let's have a look at this tummy of yours. How many times have you been sick?'

When I said 'too many', he laughed.

'Are you constipated, my dear?'

I shook my head, my cheeks flushed with embarrassment.

'When was your last period, eh?' All the time his enormous hands were kneading and prodding my stomach very gently. When I flinched, he apologized. 'Can't remember, eh? Well, we're in February now, so was it this month or January? December? November?'

'I think it was around the beginning of December, but I can't really remember. It was before Christmas I think.' My voice was a whisper and tears leaked from the sides of my eyes, slowly making their way towards my ears. Why was he so interested in my periods? Yes, they were usually once a month, but I didn't count the exact day, I found myself telling him irritably.

'I want to take a sample of your urine. Do you think you could pass a little water into this bottle for me? Not now. I'll leave it here and maybe your parents can bring it up to the surgery. Now I'm going to give you something for the pain and you must drink only plain boiled water. I'll be back to see you this afternoon. These medicines will help your temperature go down and stop the sickness. Now I'm going to give you a little injection – it'll soon see that pain off and it'll make you sleepy.'

He had turned his back on me and when he turned around I saw the glint of a large hypodermic syringe in the February sunshine. He rolled up my pyjama sleeve and the tiny prick he'd promised felt more like the jab of a knitting needle.

I thanked him and he smiled and said I was the first person to thank him for hurting them.

'What's the matter with me, doctor? Why does it hurt so much? Do you think I've got cancer?'

'Good Lord no! I would say you've got a nasty old bout of colic. Having suffered from it myself, I know how bad the pain is, and maybe you've one of these

273

nasty bugs that're going round. When are you due to take your examinations? June? My son is sitting his and he has every ailment under the sun, which I should say goes under the heading of pre-examination nerves. He's like a cat . . .'

His voice began to recede far away, the pain became a dull ache and I drifted into oblivion.

I was aware of Kathleen Oakes occasionally and annoyingly bringing me sips of water that tasted like Blimp's coat when he was wet. I vaguely remember the doctor being called back upstairs as I was being sick again. Mrs Oakes gave me the medicine, which usually made me sick and rudely interrupted my sleep, but sleep I did. Eventually I stopped being sick. Marion Knightley kissed me goodbye, but I didn't remember her entrance, so her exit confused me.

The following morning the doctor came and although my stomach was still tender all over, that awful pain had gone. He insisted that I continue to take drinks, and said I could have lemon and barley water now and maybe some weak tea that evening.

When I awoke the following morning, the pain was gone. My heart leapt as I saw Gordon standing by my bed with a cup of tea in his hand, which was trembling, causing the crockery to sing and the tea to dribble down the side of the cup. I took the cup and saucer from him in silence and waited for him to leave. He stood towering above me as I leaned on one elbow and tried to steady my own trembling hand.

'Um . . . you feeling better? Ma says maybe you can have a lightly boiled egg today.'

He made it sound as if I had been awarded a prize for gallantry, but I pulled a face at the thought of a smelly boiled egg being placed before me.

'Eh . . . Ma says that your stomach's swollen and you haven't had your, er . . . monthly cycle. That's what she says.'

I remained silent.

'The doc was worried about you . . . Christ, Callie, what's going to happen if you're going to have a kid?' His voice had risen to near hysteria and he sat down at the foot of my bed, pushing his hands up over his temples. I saw with sudden clarity that Gordon was spineless.

I can honestly say that throughout the years of his 'tailing' me the thought of my becoming pregnant had never entered my mind, and I was stunned into further silence by Gordon's diagnosis. My thoughts raced to Cherry, but surely both people had to participate willingly, as Cherry had, for a baby to be conceived. Cherry had talked and giggled about her sexual activities, and so had Frances, a girl at school who'd left to have a baby. One of the girls who'd been in the year above me was married, and I'd seen her pushing her pram and had admired her baby. Was it a boy or a girl? I couldn't remember. Gordon's hand tapping at my shins through the bedclothes brought me back from this mêlée of thoughts to the trauma I was facing.

'No periods, swollen stomach . . . Callie, oh God, Callie, surely you can see what this means?'

'Does it mean that I am . . . Have they said so?' My voice was strangled.

'No, but Christ, Callie, can't you see what this could mean? Jesus Christ, what will they do to me? I could go to prison, you're under age and . . . oh Christ, I know for a fact that if I get done, I'll . . . you get to have a lot of accidents "inside" for things like this, and the prison officers turn their backs while the real criminals nearly smash your brains in. Oh, Callie, don't say it was me. I'll do away with myself. Callie, you know I love you. Can't you say it was a boy who's left school now? Say you were raped or I'll kill myself.'

As I lay there terrified, watching him sweep tear-stained palms through his temples and over his crown, I knew that I wanted to kill him.

Let me borrow your axe, Gordon. It won't take years of hacking away at the young sapling. I promise it will be swift, Gordon. Why, I could even give you a few tips, Gordon – watch the walnut! Watch it as the first crack of the weapon strikes, strikes it open. The walnut is old now, Gordon, inside the shell the crisp, pale-brown kernel has become a blackened husk. The husk that is you, Gordon, crumbling, crumbling into the ashes of death, Gordon.

'Get out, get out!' The weakness in my body had not affected my vocal cords, and the menace in the voice that rasped out this order frightened me as I realized it came from my own throat. I didn't look at him, but heard him get up, an ugly snuffling sound passing above my head, as he meekly obeyed and left the room.

I threw myself wholeheartedly into my schoolwork, and my weekends were taken up with the store. Jane continued to call and often asked questions about my happiness and lack of social life, as she put it. My health had been on the agenda too, but since I had made a complete recovery – my stomach distension had subsided and my monthly cycle had reappeared – she abandoned the subject.

I was delighted to find that I had done well in my examinations, with the exception of maths and geography, and I was overjoyed to walk away with 120 w.p.m. in shorthand and 60 w.p.m. in typing. The only other person to have attained my shorthand speed was a boy who wanted to be a journalist. I was given the choice of the best jobs available through the school, and everyone was surprised at my daring when I went for an interview to an association in St James's Street, right in the middle of London. A position as junior shorthand typist was offered to me and I was ecstatic. I was less ecstatic when I said goodbye to my friends on the last day of school.

The sun beat down as we made our solemn promise on the bank of the school field that we'd meet on this day each year at a restaurant. Some of the students were staying on to take their A levels. I said a tearful farewell to my English teacher, a wonderful Welshman, who condemned the stupid, bloody bureaucracy that stopped me from going on to do A levels too.

Pauline had got a job as a junior typist in a solicitor's office not far from the store, and she and I would continue to see each other. With Dee and Derek's wedding not far off and my job in London, Dee had asked me to look round the bridal stores, and then the three of us would go up for the day to choose our dresses.

My last night at the store was a sad one for me, and I promised that I would call in on a Saturday and 'keep my hand in'. I was not prepared for the staff's presentation of a trendy handbag with a matching purse, which contained a five-pound note. They called me a 'city slicker' and wished me well. I cried all the way home on the bus even though I knew I'd see most of them on my Saturdays off. Still, I felt a sense of loss. I would be seeing them, but only as an outsider. They had been more than friends and colleagues; they had made me part of a family, and the tie was not easily broken.

Gordon and his father kept a respectful distance from me now, and I was never 'topped' or 'tailed' by either of them again. Mrs Oakes, proud of the status working in Central London conferred on me, would often ask me to pop into Harrods or Fortnum and Mason for the most ridiculous items. These errands could be accomplished only by some swift legwork, but she seemed to think London was as small as her own town.

I now joined the commuters who I had waved to when I delivered newspapers. The journey was long and arduous. I took sandwiches and would eat them in St James's Park. Sometimes, if it were raining my lunchtime would be spent browsing in Burlington Arcade.

Jane still visited, but very rarely and usually when I'd just arrived home exhausted. The house now smelled unpleasantly of birds' droppings and musty seeds, as the lounge had been turned into an aviary. One evening at the beginning of August, while I was laboriously chewing my way through a salad, Jane called. I hadn't got home until after seven o'clock and I was rather irritated when Mrs Oakes put her head around the dining-room door and announced that I'd 'got a visitor'. I thrust my plate away bad-temperedly and arose to find myself looking into Jane's beaming face.

'Hi! I've got something for you. It couldn't wait. Here! Gosh, you look bushed. Enjoying the job?'

I took the letter that she held out to me and said that I was, but the journey was hell. As I opened the envelope, addressed in a spidery scrawl, pure joy caused all my tiredness to evaporate, and before I could drink in the words, I danced around the room. The letter was from my grandmother.

She thanked me for the lovely tablecloth I had made, and said she expected I was a big girl now and she couldn't wait to see me. She had a special friend and was keeping in good health, considering. There wasn't much money around but she'd 'make do and mend' as always. When could she see me and did I look like my mummy? She still smoked Weights and she sent all her love and kisses, signing herself 'Ganny'. Kisses climbed up and down the bottom of the page, an ink-drenched, sun-drenched spider trail of love.

After I'd finished my Hiawatha dance around the dining-room, my questions came tumbling, spilling, waiting for Jane to answer everything that was spinning around in my brain.

'I made that tablecloth ages ago, but she'd moved. It was years ago. Miss Crowley said she'd give it to her. She didn't, did she? The old bitch didn't give it to her, Jane, did she?' My voice rose in anger and I asked Jane if she'd tell me where Gran had moved to. When she said my grandmother hadn't moved, I had to sit down. I was breathless, I wanted to go now, this minute, to see her!

'Listen, my love, don't think too badly of Miss Crowley. People do things differently, that's all. She thought it for the best to keep it in the office. She wanted what was best for you. She wanted you to settle in here. Don't be angry. Just think of it this way, it got held up in the post, but it reached its destination eventually.'

That night I couldn't sleep, and I was up at five the next morning.

'Can I have my Post Office savings book? I want to buy Granny some cigarettes and presents.' The urgency in my voice couldn't be contained, but Arthur Oakes just sat at the dining-table reading his paper. I looked at the clock, afraid that I'd miss my train. I repeated my question and tapped at the newspaper.

Without a word he got up and slowly left the room. I heard him mount the stairs, then come down again. Finally, with great deliberation, he strolled back into the room. My eyes were on the clock and I knew I wouldn't catch the train. Panic seized me as he began to slap the thin book in the palm of his hand.

'It's a great pity you couldn't have thought about buying Mums a present, or doesn't she count now that you've found your precious grandmother? After all that woman's done for you! My God, we took you in, gave you all the comforts you'd never known before. You should remember what we took you from, your father and all –'

'Don't say anything about my father, don't you dare, or any of my family! They'd kill you if they knew what's happened to me here.'

'Oh, so the daughter of the Irish peasant who treated her so well is now so protective. It's amazing what six feet of earth can do for man's status.'

'I hate you! You could go to prison for what you've done to me in this house, you wicked bastards!' I screamed.

'Dad, for Christ's sake, you've gone a bit too far, haven't you?'

Gordon put out a hand to stop me, but I ran blindly from the room, snatching up the savings book Mr Oakes had thrown at me. I had two suitcases on top of the wardrobe, one a mottled grey and the other a small brown cardboard one. I pushed everything I could into them, including, of course, my scarf and envelope and annual. I couldn't take my winter clothes, only some cardigans and a tartan suit. I grabbed my mac and two pairs of shoes. I looked at my alarm clock and guiltily packed that too. The contents of my years in care were crammed into those two suitcases and sadly I descended the stairs. I could hear Mrs Oakes crying in the kitchen.

'It's all that bloody jumped-up bitch from the Welfare's fault,' she wailed. She had been upstairs when the row erupted.

'I'm sorry, Mm. Please, you don't understand everything. I'll write to you.' I was crying now.

'I understand this much, ducks, that you and God himself can't come between me and my men. Where will you live?'

'With Granny. I'm going to miss you and I do appreciate –'

'Don't say any more, ducks, just go. And look after yourself.'

I carried the cases and my 'city slicker' handbag into freedom and later that afternoon into the arms of my grandmother.

23

Granny looked better than she had when I'd last seen her. I met her coming out of the house on her way to meet her friend in a sleazy café. Her friend looked to be as sleazy as the café, and when I was told he had a room above, it seemed a fitting habitat for this non-descript little man with a weasel face, brown hair greased back and small brown eyes that looked like old-fashioned shoe-buttons. I deposited my suitcases by the table and George, who had taken my hand and kissed it, ordered egg and chips for the three of us. It had begun to rain when we took our leave of George. He kissed my hand for the second time, which made me realize I'd not packed any toiletries. He kissed Granny's hand too and said, 'Same time, same place tomorrow.' He smiled, exposing remarkably good teeth, and walked us to the door.

'He's proposed to me, you know, darling, but I don't want to rush things. He's a nice man, gassed in the Great War, you know, medals for gallantry too, he'll show them to you. Here, let's have a good look at you.'

Relieved to put the suitcases down, I stopped as Gran scrutinized my face.

'I don't know whether you're more like your mummy or ... uh ... his lordship. Different colouring, his I suppose.' She sniffed her disapproval of my genetic fail-ings and then, peering at me with further intensity pronounced, 'No, it's our side you take after. Pretty as a picture, what's wrong with me? If you had her brown eyes, you'd be . . .' Her voice tailed off and I took it as a cue to pick up my suitcases again. We trudged a short distance along the road to her house.

'George likes you,' she whispered as we climbed the steps to her front door. 'I only wish *she* could have lived to see . . .' Her sentence unfinished, she turned the key in the lock and the familiar smell of mothballs and gas and cooked cabbage assailed my nostrils. The stairs were unlit and dark, even though it was afternoon, admittedly a dull and rainy one.

I couldn't believe how tiny her attic room was. I'd become used to light, spacious rooms. I put my suitcases near the old wooden washstand and watched Gran light a match under the kettle on the single gas ring in the hearth. She struck another match, pulled the chain level and the gas light plopped on as the flame touched the tiny perforated bulb. The room took on a saffron hue and the tinny old kettle began to hiss on the rusty ring.

Drinking from a cracked cup, Gran asked what I'd want for tea. I said I'd go to the shop on the corner and get some groceries and, seeing her pick up her packet of ten Players Weights and frown, told her I wouldn't forget her Weights for the world. I telephoned the office and said I'd be off work today and tomorrow, inventing a fictitious illness, which, the way I was feeling, wasn't quite so fictitious. I could smell Granny's house on my clothes now and wondered how I could live there and not smell of it.

As I left the shop I felt a tremendous sense of loss for the house I had shared for so long and the realization that I would never be Dee's bridesmaid now. I fought back bitter tears as I returned to Granny's tiny attic room. How fickle was my heart! The place, this place, my London, seemed alien, and I knew that I was going through a reversal of the adjustment I had made when I first went to the Oakeses. I vaguely wondered what song Kathleen Oakes would be singing on this day. I knew it wouldn't be 'Everything's in Rhythm with My Heart'. Perhaps it was John Hanson's 'Goodbye'.

Granny was burning sticks of wood and putting small nuggets of coal into the black stove that also served as a tiny oven and hotplate. Her face lit up when she saw me and I saw her eyes widen as I placed forty Players Weights on the tiny table near her bed. I'd bought some sad-looking salad and four wrinkled apples, bread, butter, chocolate finger-biscuits and a small tin of pink salmon.

That night, as I lay on the bed against the wall in the stale old room tainted with gas and the suffocating heat from the black stove, Granny lay down by my side without bothering to undress. I felt her arm reach over and stroke my face.

'Granny, did you miss me?' I asked.

'Course I missed you, darling. Don't let's talk about what's past. The main thing is you're back with Ganny. George says the past upsets me too much and I mustn't dwell on it. I have my funny turns. The best thing is you're here with Ganny, and they've made a lovely young lady out of you in that home, smart as paint and pretty as a picture. Tomorrow I'll go and ask Lady Muck downstairs if a pound a week is enough for you to stay.'

I held on to the tiny thin-skinned hand with its coarse fingernails and kissed it. This was what it was all about.

I was here with Granny and I was safe, I was where I belonged. If I had one wish, it would be that God could pluck the house I'd left that morning from the ground and place it here, where Granny could see the fruit trees and the beautiful flowers that grew in the garden. She and I could share what had been 'my room' and we'd live happily ever after.

'Lady Muck', as Granny referred to the landlady of the house, had told her that she was trying to decrease the number of lodgers she had, not increase them. Some gentlemen had offered her a good price for the house, and, 'Blackie Beetle' in the basement, Miss Walters on the second floor and my grandmother were the only three people standing in the way of her spending her twilight years in a small cottage somewhere.

Granny cussed and swore, and once again I heard about the landlady's mother having been in service in Granny's parents' house.

'Married above her station, same as my gel married beneath hers. I can't believe she was taken so young ...' Granny cried and so did I in our common bond of grief for my dead mother.

'When you're living down in poverty street, nobody knocks at your door, when you're living down in poverty street, the folks all say you're poor, but when you're living down in Golden Square, they come around all day ... She was a sweet little dicky bird, cheep! cheep! cheep! she went. Gaily she sang to me till all my money was spent. Then she went off song, we parted on fighting terms, she was one of the early birds and I was one of the worms ...' Granny rocked me in her arms and sang the songs I'd forgotten. I was safe and back in time with her familiar, if rather unusual choice of, lullabies.

I found a bed-sit near Kentish Town and spent my first week sleeping between blankets and on a pillow without a pillowcase. I didn't realize such things wouldn't be provided. A pair of candy-striped sheets and a towel made a hole in my Post Office savings. I bought Nescafé and Farley's Rusks and, having only a gas ring and one saucepan, lived on a diet of soup and baked beans, but mostly rusks. I had to buy my own toilet paper, and a bath cost a shilling.

My bed-sitter was on the second floor of a very large house and the toilet that served the second and third floors was next to it. Most of the tenants were Irish and men, and it was rather unnerving to hear the toilet being used incessantly at night. This noise and occasionally the unpleasant sound of someone vomiting, the singing and the occasional bump against my door from someone who'd had too much to drink made me ensure that my door was always locked and a chair placed under the doorknob for added security. I decided that once inside my room it would be wisest to stay there, so my next vital purchase was a pink baby's potty, which enabled me to answer any call of nature that would otherwise force me out of my lair.

I was always treated with extreme courtesy by the other tenants, who seemed to have come from all over the Emerald Isle – Galway, Cork, Dublin, Kilkenny and Kildare. I was invited out for a drink by one or two if we chanced to meet on a Saturday or Sunday morning when I went off to see Granny and George. I was also very happy in my work and had a lovely boss, who, I thought, was the most beautiful woman I had ever seen. Her husband worked for the association too, and seemed very old and staid in comparison. She knew that

I now lived in London, but I never told her what my accommodation consisted of. I think she believed I was living in my grandmother's house, and I am sure she would have helped me had she known my plight. Instead of getting used to the house and the other lodgers, I grew more nervous.

I bought the *Evening Standard* to look for a more suitable place to live and under 'Situations Vacant' saw what I was sure would solve all my problems: an opening for a young person with the necessary qualifications for hotel management training; accommodation was available with the job. I travelled to the beautiful riverside town where the hotel was located – my first impression was how tiny all the streets and houses were – for an interview on Saturday. I was told there and then that I'd got the job and asked how soon I could start. On Sunday afternoon I found myself being shown into a beautiful room, which, although at the top of the hotel, was a guest room, as I was considered 'Management Staff'.

It was in this hotel that I found what I had missed for so long – friends, security and freedom. I soaked up the work like a sponge; the hours were long and happy. Although I did stints as chambermaid, waitress and sometimes in the bar or the enormous kitchens with the chefs, it was reception and the administrative side that became my forte.

I became friendly with a German waitress and asked the manager if it would be possible for me to share her room, as another waitress had just left. He readily agreed. If our shifts allowed, Inge and I would sometimes go into the town during the day to shop, but mostly we would meet at night, exhausted, feast from a tray of luxuries Inge'd brought up from the kitchen, then crash out on our beds, listening to Radio Luxembourg. Life was wonderful and I visited my grandmother as often as my shifts would allow.

I hadn't been at the hotel very long when I woke Inge in the middle of the night with a recurrence of the pain I'd had in February. I was vomiting badly and had a fever. A concerned Management gave me brandy, which made me even sicker. The hotel doctor was called out and an ambulance was sent for immediately. I was operated on the following day for a large ovarian cyst, and the surgeon told me he took away a nasty old appendix too. The fears of any pregnancy by the axe-man did not exist and I was overwhelmed by the flowers and cards I received from staff and clientele alike.

Within months of my discharge from hospital, I was married to one of the patrons of the hotel who had sent me flowers. However, a dark cloud hung over my horizon. It was discovered that I had no legal guardian and would have to go to Somerset House to get copies of my parents' death certificates and my own birth certificate. I would then be made a ward of court and permission for the marriage could be granted.

That morning in Somerset House it looked as though my birth certificate couldn't be found: either the 'O' had been dropped from my surname, O'Farrell, or it had been deleted in error. By the time this was sorted out I was in floods of tears.

My fiancé was slightly bemused by my distress. My parents' death certificates were easily found, and that evening, clutching my mother's death certificate in my hand, I went to see my doctor, ostensibly for a post-operative check-up. It was with trembling hands that I handed him my mother's death certificate. The cause of death on the certificate was a 'right frontal glioma'. The doctor explained to me that my mother had died of a malignant brain tumour, and the two previous operations on her brain that I had told him about reinforced his opinion that no one could have saved her. A blow by a child's elbow could in no way have accelerated her death, he assured me.

'Oh, doctor, thank you, thank you so much, I'll never forget you,' I told this very bewildered general practitioner whose hand I had grasped so firmly. Check-up forgotten, I bounced out of his surgery and down to the hotel where I was to meet my future husband. He was amusing a crowd of his friends by recounting that morning's visit to Somerset House.

'She was in tears, floods of tears – thought you didn't exist, did you, my sweet?' Everyone laughed, and I nodded and joined in their laughter. I was to be teased about that many times.

Within the next two years my happiness knew no bounds, as the birth of my first-born, a beautiful baby girl, was followed by that of my first son. So much had been taken from me for so many years and now it was being given back. In the words of that song heard so long ago by the orange glow of a radiogram, someone had watched over me.

My grandmother lived to see her first two great-grandchildren, whom she adored. She died a week after our last visit to her in the old people's home in Highgate, where she spent her last days in comfort and happiness. Her refusal to come and live with me or to transfer to an equally comfortable home for the elderly near me was emphatic. No, she couldn't leave London. Move to foreign shores at her time of life? Unthinkable! The foreign shores of Berkshire? She wouldn't be able to understand 'their' language over there anyway.

The Stars Burn On

Denise Robertson

On New Year's Day 1980, Jenny and seven friends watch the dawn from a northern hill. On the brink of adulthood, confident of their futures, they vow to meet there again at the end of the decade. Just two weeks later, one of the group is dead. The others, irrevocably affected, go on to pursue careers in the law or media, and make new lives for themselves as husbands, wives and parents. Jenny, who establishes herself as a successful journalist in London, remains their lynchpin – and only Jenny knows that the secret that binds them is a lie.

'A saga that'll keep you turning the pages ... told with perception and humour' – *Prima*

'Her prose has a fine flow, her knowledge of the region is deep and instinctive. Above all, her compassion and great understanding of life show in all she writes' – *Evening Chronicle*, Newcastle on Tyne

Published or forthcoming

SIGNET

THE RATING GAME

Dave Cash

Behind the glass-fronted walls of CRFM's 24-hours-a-day nerve centre in the heart of London, three people fight for control of their lives as the tycoon powerbrokers of international finance move in for the kill...

Monica Hammond, the radio station's beautiful and ruthless Managing Director – nothing was allowed to stand in her way ... until one man discovered her fatal weakness.

Nigel Beresford-Clarke – CRFM's greatest asset – hopelessly betrayed by his love for a schoolgirl...

And **Maggie Lomax**, uncompromising and tough as nails – then her outspoken broadcasts pushed the wrong people too far ...

They're ready to play ... *The Rating Game*

Published or forthcoming

Ira Levin
author of *Rosemary's Baby*

Thirteen hundred Madison Avenue, an elegant 'sliver' building, soars high and narrow over Manhattan's smart Upper East Side. Kay Norris, a successful single woman, moves on to the twentieth floor of the building, high on hopes of a fresh start and the glorious Indian summer outside. But she doesn't know that someone is listening to her. Someone is *watching* her.

'Levin really knows how to touch the nerve ends' – *Evening Standard*

'*Sliver* is the ultimate *fin de siècle* horror novel, a fiendish goodbye-wave to trendy urban living ... Ira Levin has created the apartment dweller's worst nightmare' – Stephen King

Published or forthcoming

Liscombe Hall

Anne Griffiths

When an illicit liaison with Lord Liscombe ends in heartbreak, Kate Tranter sets out in search of a new life. Driven to protect a secret borne of passion, she rises beyond her humble beginnings to become a wealthy restaurateur; indomitable, proud, admired – and haunted by the searing memory of a love that could never be.

Set amidst the rolling hills of the Dorset countryside, from the turn of the century to the post-war era, *Liscombe Hall* follows the tangled destinies of two families and the powerful passions that bind them.

SIGNET

Published or forthcoming

HAVING IT ALL

Maeve Haran

Having it All. Power. Money. Success. *And* a happy family. Liz really believed she could have it all. So when she's offered one of the most important jobs in television, she jumps at it.

But Liz discovers that there's a price to be paid for her success and that the whole glittering image is just an illusion. And one day she's faced with the choice she thought she'd never have to make.

Liz decides she *will* have it all — but on her own terms.

'Will touch cords, tug heartstrings. Every woman's been here' – Penny Vincenzi, author of *Old Sins*

'Realistic, compassionate, but still as pacey as they come' – *Cosmopolitan*

SIGNET

Published or forthcoming

UNAUTHORIZED

Christopher Andersen

'Power is a great aphrodisiac, and I'm a very powerful person ...' are the words of the highest-paid woman in show business.

The words of Madonna. Self-made icon. The most famous woman in the world. But how did she do it? And what *really* happened along the way?

MADONNA: UNAUTHORIZED
looks beyond the carefully constructed public image of a star who has clocked up more hit singles than the Beatles.

More shocking than anything she has so far dared to reveal...

MADONNA: UNAUTHORIZED
covers it all, from abortion to AIDS, from marriage and Marilyn to men she forgot, from women and Warren to ruling the world...

'Compulsive ... the controversies, the triumphs, the lovers ... diligently chronicled'
– *Observer*